U-STARS~PLUS

Science & Literature Connections

*Using **Science, Talents,** and **Abilities** to **Recognize Students~Promoting Learning** for **Underrepresented Students***

Mary Ruth Coleman, Ph.D.

Sneha Shah-Coltrane, M.A.

Library of Congress Cataloging-in-Publication Data

U-STARS~PLUS Science & Literature Connections
2nd printing
p. cm.
Includes bibliographical references (p.)

ISBN 0-86586-454-3 (paper)

Front cover artwork by George E. Miller II, *Hands on Science: Discovering the Possibilities*, © 2003, www.gemartstudio.com, 1 (904) 521-4059.

Design & Layout: Carol L. Williams

Stock No. P5968

Printed in the United States of America.

10 9 8 7 6 5 4 3 2

Table of Contents

Science & Literature Connections

Table of Contents (cont'd)

About the Authors

Mary Ruth Coleman, Ph.D.

Mary Ruth Coleman is Senior Scientist Emeritus at the FPG Child Development Institute at the University of North Carolina at Chapel Hill, and a Research Associate Professor in the School of Education. She directed Project *U-STARS~PLUS* (Using Science, Talents, and Abilities to Recognize Students~Promoting Learning in Underrepresented Students), and project ACCESS (Achievement in Content and Curriculum for Every Student's Success). She was Co-Principal Investigator for the Early Learning Disabilities Initiative sponsored by the Emily Hall Tremaine Foundation. Dr. Coleman has numerous publications including the seminal textbook, *Educating Exceptional Children*, 12th edition, (Kirk, Gallagher, Coleman, and Anastasiow, 2008). She has served three terms (9 years) on the Board of Directors for The Association for Gifted (TAG), one of which she was President; three terms (9 years) on the Board of the National Association for Gifted Children (NAGC); and two terms (6 years) on the Board of Directors for the Council for Exceptional Children (CEC). She was president of CEC in 2007.

Sneha Shah-Coltrane, M.A.

Sneha Shah-Coltrane is currently the North Carolina Department of Public Instruction's State Consultant for Academically/Intellectually Gifted. Prior to this, she was Co-Director of Project *U-STARS~PLUS*. She works in all aspects of her professional life to better cultivate, recognize, and serve gifted students in the classroom, especially those students whose potential has been historically overlooked. Ms. Shah-Coltrane has worked on these issues as an elementary classroom teacher, a researcher, a professional development creator and presenter, and as a leader in professional organizations. Her service to the field has included work as Chair of the Early Childhood Division of the NAGC and she is currently a member of the Board of Directors for CEC-TAG.

Acknowledgments

We express our sincere gratitude to the many individuals who contributed to the work of *U-STARS~PLUS* (Using Science, Talents, and Abilities to Recognize Students~Promoting learning for Underrepresented Students) over the years. First we acknowledge the Javits Grants for Gifted and Talented Education and the Z. Smith Reynolds Foundation whose funding made this work possible.

We would like to thank the following members of the *U-STARS~PLUS* team at the FPG Child Development Institute of University of North Carolina at Chapel Hill for their work over the years of development: Christine Harradine, Lisé Timmons, Matt McBee, Reid Adams, Carla Smith, Emily King, Feihong Wang, Toni Glatz, Cindy Reid, Crystal De la Cruz, Debbie Saddler, Jennifer Job, Blair Payne, Patricia McConnell, and Jill Barker. We also gratefully acknowledge the FPG support team members in Statistics and Design: Eloise Neebe and Stephen Magers; Publications and Outreach: Pam Winton, Gina Harrison, and Michael Brady; the Business Office: Amy Crume and Jana Spaugh; and Technology Support: Wendy Webber and Kevin Gunn. A special thanks goes to Sam Odom, Director of the FPG Child Development Institute for his leadership and support over the years.

U-STARS~PLUS would not have been possible without the dedication of our collaborative partners in schools across the country. We thank our partner school districts:

North Carolina:
Asheboro City, Asheville City, Cabarrus County, Chapel Hill-Carrboro City, Cherokee Reservation, Craven County, Davidson County, Davie County, Edenton-Chowan County, Edgecombe County, Kannapolis City, Madison County, Nash-Rocky Mount County, Northampton County, Orange County, Pender County, Rutherford County, and Wake County.

Colorado:
Adams 27J-Brighton, Arapahoe 5/Cherry Creek, Cheyenne County, Lake County, Mesa County, Montezuma-Cortez, Poudre, and St. Vrain Valley.

Louisiana:
St. Landry Parish

Ohio:
Cincinnati Public Schools, Mt. Healthy City, North College Hills City, Norwood City, and Reading, as part of Hamilton County Educational Services Center

We appreciate the guidance and science content expertise of the Morehead Planetarium and Science Center with the leadership of Denise Young, Director of Education Programs. We are thankful for the collaborative spirit of our colleagues Jacqueline Medina, Deborah Rothenberg, Sherri Samuels, Karren Ryder, Lucille Hollier, and Cathy Reed, each of whom helped to shape the work across the country, making it better and richer.

We wish to thank the dedicated CEC staff who saw this project through from conception to birth: Stefani Roth, Carol Williams, Jose Maquen, Meridee Mucciarone, and Marcia Freeman. We also thank Deborah Whitley, Lorraine Sobson, Tom Karabatakis, and Marcia Kennedy for their editorial eye in helping to polish the work. The contributions of each of these individuals strengthened the work in so many ways.

We also thank our mentors, James J. Gallagher and Ann Harrison, for their continued guidance and support over the years.

And as always, we are grateful to our families for their support and endurance.

Mary Ruth Coleman
Sneha Shah-Coltrane
University of North Carolina at Chapel Hill
2010

Forewords from the National Association for Gifted Children and The Association for the Gifted

As educators, let's think big and reach for the stars! Finding and supporting academic talent is the goal of every educator, but it has been difficult to see talent in some of our nation's poor and/or rural schools. Often, we don't see the curiosity, the advanced thinking or the quick minds of our students because of their inability to read, their lack of class participation, or their poor performance on tests. Until recently, we did not know how to search out those gifted low-income and/or minority students, but now, thanks to grants from the Jacob K. Javits Gifted and Talented Students Program and the dedication of many teachers and researchers, we now have tools for talent identification in diverse populations of learners. One tool is *U-STARS~PLUS*, a supplemental science curriculum.

Science is intriguing to both children and adults, so what could be a better match than sending science home with your students? *U-STARS~PLUS* supports science learning and the identification of students who have an early talent for science at school, but it is also designed to engage parents or guardians as partners at home.

Any home can be a science laboratory, and with the support of *U-STARS~PLUS* materials, any parent or guardian can be a science coach. *The U-STARS~PLUS* approach capitalizes on the excitement of young children and adults sharing a science learning experience. *U-STARS~PLUS* offers educators a way to connect with the families of young children who are excited about science.

U-STARS~PLUS offers teachers a way to use popular children's literature selections to highlight scientific concepts being studied, along with ideas of in-school and at-home, experiments to extend and enrich student understanding. We're confident, based on the research in gifted and talented education, science education, and early child education, that *U-STARS~PLUS* will enhance outreach efforts to families, creating and sustaining an enthusiasm for learning science and encouraging a new appreciation of scientific thought and inquiry in classrooms and at home.

Ann Robinson, Ph.D.
President of the National
Association for Gifted Children

Forewords from the National Association for Gifted Children and The Association for the Gifted

U-STARS~PLUS offers educators an opportunity to recognize and support students with potential from underserved populations. Already implemented in over 30 school districts, this comprehensive program offers hands-on science curriculum with correlated activities, teacher observation tools for identifying talents, activities for developing family partnerships, and professional development.

All of these components work together in attaining the *U-STARS~PLUS* goals: (a) developing the talents of young children from diverse backgrounds using a hands-on/ inquiry science curriculum, (b) strengthening teachers' observation skills so that more students "at-potential" will be identified for and served in gifted programs, (c) creating responsive environments that provide high-end learning opportunities for nurturing potential, (d) involving families so that their children will succeed in school, and (e) building an infrastructure to support systemic change. This comprehensive program addresses the four action areas outlined in The Association for the Gifted's (TAG) monograph, *Diversity and Developing Gifts and Talents: A National Call for Action* (see http://www.cectag.org). These areas include preparing school personnel, ensuring equitable curriculum and learning environments, finding giftedness, and including diversity in research.

The Association for the Gifted supports *U-STARS~PLUS* and believes that when these areas are addressed, educators will view students from diverse backgrounds differently and recognize that diversity and excellence are not incompatible.

Susan K. Johnsen, Ph. D.
President of The Association for the Gifted

Introduction

U-STARS~PLUS: Using-Science, Talents, and Abilities to Recognize Students~ Promoting Learning for Underrepresented Students

> Passionate educators with issue expertise can make all the difference, enabling hands-on learning that truly engages students — including girls and underrepresented minorities — and preparing them to tackle the grand challenges of the 21st century such as increasing energy independence, improving people's health, protecting the environment, and strengthening national security.
>
> ~***President Barack Obama,*** January 6, 2010

The *U-STARS~PLUS (Using-Science, Talents, and Abilities to Recognize Students~Promoting Learning for Underrepresented Students) Science & Literature Connections* was developed to bring together two critical and exciting teaching areas: science and language arts. Although these classroom support materials were originally designed for teachers working with U-STARS~PLUS, they can be used in any elementary class where the teacher hopes to inspire learning through connecting reading with high-interest science topics. *Science & Literature Connections* is based on high-quality children's books that feature science content (Bjork, 2005; Cherry, 2006). The science concepts, highlighted by each book, are based on the National Science Education Standards (1996) and will align with most states' science standards. *Science & Literature Connections* was designed for Grades K to 3; however, many of the "connections" may be adapted for Grades 4 to 5.

Each of the 32 children's books was included because it provides a wonderful platform for exploring scientific ideas within the context of excellent literature. Most of the selected books should be readily available in the school's media center and many of the books have been translated into Spanish. The books and activities are intended to be used in conjunction with a larger science unit of study, although they may be used independently as well. *Science & Literature Connections* is organized around Bloom's Taxonomy (Bloom, Krathwohl, & Masia, 1956) to support a range of thinking levels and to scaffold learning (Cheong, 2000). Thus, by using these materials, a teacher can create a higher-level thinking environment around literature connected with science.

Science & Literature Connections was designed with teachers in mind. To make them easy to use, each Connection includes

1. A list of major science topics that can be explored with the book;
2. A list of science standards drawn from the National Science Education Standards (1996);
3. A book summary providing the main ideas;
4. A science concept map showing related ideas for study;
5. A list of thinking questions based on Bloom's Taxonomy (note: these are discussion starters and were not intended to be asked all at one time, in one sitting, but used as deemed appropriate); and
6. A set of follow-up activities for students to extend their learning.

How Would These Materials Help You in Your Classroom?

The following ideas show how teachers have integrated these materials into their curriculum and instruction. Teachers who have worked with these materials

- Use the Connections as part of a larger unit of study for optimal integration and, on occasion, to enhance a stand-alone book experience.
- Use the discussion starters and activities during whole group, small group, or individual interactions to extend and enrich learning and nurture students' interest in learning.
- Use the discussion starter questions and activity ideas to supplement existing units in science and/or literacy.
- Use the follow-up activities as a learning center, whole class, small group, or independent studies to make students' literacy and science studies even more meaningful and engaging learning opportunities.
- Use the materials as a base for quality homework (e.g., sending home the book with select questions for discussion or using activities as homework extensions).
- Use the Connections as the base for a family involvement program, such as Science Family Read-Along Night.
- Create "book kits" to share with other teachers (i.e., include a copy of the book, copy of the Connections, and any other ideas for learning generated by the teachers).

- Integrate the different levels of thinking across the curriculum.
- Create new Connections for additional books.

Science & Literature Connections provides a high interest, engaging way to integrate science into your literacy time. Many of the books can be used within your current reading program, making efficient use of learning time. The incorporation of science with "real-world" topics often motivates reluctant readers who are curious about the world around them (Allington, 2002; Monhardt & Monhardt, 2006). Using these materials, you can capitalize on the wealth of children's literature and students' interest in science, creating a world of learning! Although these materials can be used alone, for optimal benefit they should be used within the context of the U-STARS~PLUS approach.

Overview of *U-STARS~PLUS*

The purpose of *U-STARS~PLUS* is to help teachers recognize and nurture potential in children from our most educationally vulnerable populations, providing them access to advanced educational opportunities for improving academic achievement.

The work of *U-STARS~PLUS* is directed by five goals:

1. Provide environments which nurture the intellectual and emotional well-being of young children (Grades K–3).
2. Recognize children with outstanding potential who may be overlooked due to poverty, cultural/linguistic differences, and/or disabilities.
3. Engage families in meaningful ways that support their child's academic success.
4. Support the use of high-quality science instruction for young children (Grades K–3) as a platform to recognize and respond to their potential.
5. Respond to children's strengths by providing appropriately challenging and advanced educational experiences (high-end learning).

U-STARS~PLUS is designed to help schools address the needs of children with high potential from educationally vulnerable populations. Educationally vulnerable populations include children from economically disadvantaged and/or culturally/linguistically diverse families and children with disabilities. Children's educational success may be jeopardized when a variety of factors combine to make school more challenging. These factors may include environmental risks, familial stressors, and individual school readiness gaps. Educationally vulnerable children, however, face their greatest risk when schools are not designed to meet their needs.

U-STARS~PLUS Philosophy and Core Beliefs

The philosophy, or "heart," of *U-STARS~PLUS* is centered on the belief that if we provide an environment that nurtures our students intellectually and emotionally, and if we observe our students systematically, we will be able to recognize our students' strengths. Recognizing a child's strengths is the first step. Once we recognize a child's strengths, we can respond to these strengths by providing advanced learning opportunities tailored to his or her needs. By looking for the strengths in our children, we reframe our view of students, moving our understanding of them from "at risk" to "at potential."

If we view our students as "at potential" versus "at risk," we can redesign their school experiences in positive ways by responding to their strengths with increasing levels of challenge. Thus the essence of *U-STARS~PLUS* is to nurture, recognize, and respond to our students, optimizing their learning and helping them thrive in our classrooms.

The core beliefs that form the foundation for *U-STARS~PLUS* are:

1. All children deserve access to challenging and enriching learning opportunities.
2. All children deserve to be viewed as "at potential" versus "at risk."
3. Science is a naturally interesting and engaging subject that captivates young children's learning.
4. Family involvement is key to sustained support for children.
5. The support we provide to a child's teacher is critical to the success of the child.

With the philosophy and core beliefs of *U-STARS~PLUS*, we lay the foundation for nurturing, recognizing, and responding to the needs of children with high potential from educationally vulnerable populations. Building on this foundation, we are able to recognize and respond to children with outstanding potential early in their school years to ensure that potential is not lost.

U-STARS~PLUS and Today's Challenging Educational Environment

The *U-STARS~PLUS* approach is particularly helpful given the challenging environment of our educational world. The challenges we face in education include the increasing intensity and range of needs that our students have (Coleman, 2000; Kirk, Gallagher, Coleman, & Anastasiow, 2009); the increasing diversity of our students' backgrounds and experiences (National Research Council, 2002); the intense impact of poverty on how children develop and on their readiness for school (Jensen, 2009); and the persistent gap in academic achievement between students who are considered the "haves" and those who are considered the "have-nots" (Barbarin, 2002; Burchinal, Peisner-Feinberg, Pianta, & Howes, 2002; Olszewski-Kubilius, Lee, Ngoi, & Ngoi, 2004). How we, as educators, address these challenges impacts all of our educationally vulnerable children, and the specific impact on children with outstanding potential is great. Our failure to address these challenges appropriately has created an environment in which educationally vulnerable children continue to be underrepresented in programs that serve children who are gifted (Ford & Harmon, 2001; Ford, Moore, & Milner, 2005).

Children from culturally/linguistically diverse families, children from economically disadvantaged families, and children with disabilities (twice exceptional learners; Briggs, Reis, & Sullivan, 2008) are educationally vulnerable and continue to be underrepresented in gifted education programs. By failing to recognize and nurture the potential of children who are educationally vulnerable, we miss a critical opportunity to provide them with support and we exacerbate the challenges the child is already facing (Gandara, 2005).

The *U-STARS~PLUS* approach is specifically designed to address these educational challenges and to reduce the disproportionate underrepresentation of educationally vulnerable students receiving gifted education services. We do this through a comprehensive set of components aimed at nurturing potential in young children so that we can recognize and respond to their needs. The five components of *U-STARS~PLUS* (see Figure 1) are:

1. High-end learning opportunities
2. Teacher's systematic observation of students
3. Hands-on, inquiry-based science
4. Family and school partnerships
5. Infrastructure building for systemic change

Figure 1. The Big Star: An Overview of *U-STARS~PLUS*

1. HIGH-END LEARNING OPPORTUNITIES

- Curriculum differentiation
  - → Curriculum compacting
  - → Tiered activities
  - → Learning centers/stations
  - → Independent studies/group projects
  - → Questioning/higher order thinking skills
- Dynamic assessment to inform classroom instruction
- Flexible grouping
- Classroom support materials:
  - → *U-STARS~PLUS Science & Literature Connections*
  - → *U-STARS~PLUS Family Science Packets*

2. TEACHERS' SYSTEMATIC OBSERVATIONS

- "At-potential" versus at-risk" mindset.
- *Teacher's Observation of Potential in Students (TOPS)*, a teacher tool to recognize students with outstanding potential from underserved populations.
- Building a body of evidence, using informal and formal measures over time.

3. HANDS-ON/INQUIRY-BASED SCIENCE

- Promotes thinking, achievement, & language development.
- Captivates students' interest through real-world setting and content integration.
- Focuses on exploration and problem. solving; not solely based on traditional expository methods/verbal skills.

4. FAMILY & SCHOOL PARTNERSHIPS

- Family involvement programs
- Effective parent conferences and communication
- *U-STARS~PLUS Family Science Packets*
- Cultural understanding (impact of poverty, diversity, and social emotional needs)

5. INFRASTRUCTURE BUILDING FOR SYSTEMIC CHANGE

- Capacity building of leadership & teachers (i.e., professional development & policy)
- Fidelity of Implementation (district, school, classroom)
- Accountability (district, school, classroom, child)

At the center of the Big Star is the cycle that we call the "heart" of *U-STARS~PLUS*: nurture/recognize/respond. We establish an intellectually and emotionally nurturing environment, we recognize the strengths of our children, and we respond to these strengths by providing enriched and challenging learning experiences that further nurture the child and lead to additional opportunities to recognize the child's strengths. This process is iterative and continues as long as we teach, because each time we recognize and respond to strengths within a child, we expand that child's capacity and so we must provide additional nurturing opportunities.

The five points of the star represent the five components of the *U-STARS~PLUS* approach. Each component will first be described in isolation, looking at its key elements and how it fits within the *U-STARS~PLUS* approach. However, because the true magic of this approach happens when the components are used together, we will also discuss the synergy across and among the five components.

Points of the Star: The Five Components of *U-STARS~PLUS*

1. High-End Learning Opportunities

Teacher expectations are key to establishing an environment where children have access to meaningful learning experiences (Ford, 2004; Rubie-Davies, 2007). If we believe that children can think with complexity, have important and interesting questions, and can learn meaningful and powerful things, then we will create an environment that supports children in these ways (Coleman, 2003; 2005). We as teachers make choices every day about what and how we will teach. These choices are guided by curriculum standards, instructional materials, and pacing guides, but we, as teachers, still have a fair amount of discretionary space to shape the learning experiences we provide in classrooms. Providing high-end learning opportunities for our children creates the intellectually nurturing environment they need (Ford & Grantham, 2003; Hertzog, 2005).

An intellectually nurturing environment in our classrooms is important for all children, but it is essential for children from educationally vulnerable populations (i.e., culturally/ linguistically diverse and economically disadvantaged and/or with disabilities) who need additional enrichment and support (Ford & Grantham, 2003). Providing enriching, meaningful, and appropriately challenging learning experiences for all students ensures access to quality instruction for all students; thus, we nurture, recognize, and respond to every student's potential (Tomlinson, Ford, Reis, Briggs, & Strickland, 2004). The intellectually nurturing environment, when combined with an emotionally nurturing environment, communicates to the child, "I believe in you, and I think you are a 'can-do kid!'" For a young child, when your teacher thinks that you are a "can-do kid," it is very hard not to believe her!

Curriculum differentiation is the first element of a high-end learning environment (Tomlinson et al., 2004). *U-STARS~PLUS* uses a basic "toolkit" of five strategies to make the general education curriculum more enriching and challenging for young children:

1. Curriculum compacting (when a child knows the material, he or she is allowed to move to something new).
2. Tiered lessons (structuring the lesson to meet the learning needs of the child for mastery, enrichment, and additional challenge).
3. Learning centers/stations (allowing for flexible grouping and small groups within the classroom).
4. Independent and small group projects (often honoring the interests of the child).
5. Questioning techniques to promote higher level thinking.

These five curriculum differentiation strategies are the foundation for differentiation in the general education classroom (Coleman, 1996; Gall, 1984; Tomlinson et, al. 2004). More information on each strategy is presented in the *U-STARS~PLUS Professional Development Kit* (Coleman & Shah-Coltrane, 2010b).

The second element of the high-end learning environment is ***Dynamic assessment to inform instruction***, the use of ongoing, dynamic assessment to inform instruction. Progress monitoring, a form of dynamic assessment, allows the teacher to collect data on the child's learning so that instruction can be modified when needed (Kirschenbaum, 1998). Progress monitoring data is often used to assess when the child needs more support for learning, but it also can be used to determine when a child needs advanced learning challenges. Using assessments to inform instruction is critical both in recognizing children's strengths and needs and in guiding the response we make to address these appropriately (Coleman, 2003; Shah-Coltrane & Coleman, 2005).

Flexible grouping is the third essential element to the high-end learning environment. Learning groups are formed based on the assessment of students' strengths and needs. Progress monitoring and other dynamic assessment strategies provide the data needed to form groups appropriately. Groups may be formed to support academic skills development, to address cognitive needs, to facilitate a child's interests, and/or to promote socialization skills (Coleman, 1994; 1998). The groups may be formed by children choosing work partners, or perhaps the "group" is just one child who works alone. The use of flexible grouping allows children to work in clusters or configurations that best match their learning needs. How these groupings are formed depends on the situation and the instructional purpose. Flexible grouping allows the teacher to design specific learning experiences for specific groups of children.

The fourth, and final, element in the high-end learning environment is the ***U-STARS~PLUS classroom support materials***: *Science & Literature Connections* and *Family Science Packets* (Coleman & Shah-Coltrane, 2010a). These materials are designed to help teachers create a high-end learning environment. The materials incorporate basic principles of differentiated instruction in concrete ways so that teachers can provide meaningfully enriched and challenging science content while simultaneously developing the ability to differentiate lessons. *Science & Literature Connections* specifically focuses on strategies to help teachers incorporate questions that elicit higher levels of thinking for their students. *Family Science Packets* (Coleman & Shah-Coltrane, 2010a) is designed to complement and extend the school's science curriculum and instruction while modeling differentiation and hands-on/inquiry-based approaches to learning. All of the *U-STARS~PLUS* science materials are based on the National Science Education Standards (1996) and are designed to align with and extend the school's science curriculum.

When children are engaged in learning through active, inquiry-based, enriched materials within a high-end learning environment, we are able to see their strengths—if we are looking for them. This high-end learning environment provides the ideal context for a teacher to use systematic observations so that a student's potential can be recognized.

2. Teachers' Systematic Observations of Students

A nurturing high-end learning environment is the critical platform from which we can systematically observe potential in our children. Once the nurturing environment has been established it becomes possible to recognize the strengths of the children through systematic and intentional observations.

There are three aspects of systematic observations:

1. Creating an "at-potential" mindset with children.
2. Using the *Teacher's Observation of Potential in Students* (*TOPS*).
3. Using the body-of-evidence approach to understand the child's needs.

The first element of teacher's systematic observation involves a shift in perspective to an ***"at-potential" mindset***: changing how we view children who come from educationally vulnerable populations (i.e., children from culturally/linguistically diverse and/or economically disadvantaged families, and children with disabilities). We have traditionally viewed these children as "at risk," and this view has promoted interventions that focus on minimizing risk and remediating deficits. The *U-STARS~PLUS* approach takes an "at-potential" view of children, focusing on maximizing children's potential by creating environments that respond to their strengths.

Although this shift in perspective may seem subtle, it is actually quite profound. Johannes Kepler (1571–1630), the famous astronomer, is reported to have said, "Be careful how you perceive the world ... it is that way." We have the power to shape our environment for better or for worse depending on how we choose to see it. When we see children as capable, interesting, and smart, this perspective is reflected to them in our words, our behaviors, and our expectations (Coleman, 2005). We also begin to shape our classrooms so that they meet the needs of children who are capable, interesting, and smart. For years we have understood that our expectations of our students are directly related to their actions, performances, and success in school. When children see us "seeing them" in these ways, they tend to believe us—and so they begin to become even more capable, interesting, and smart! In this way, through our recognition of their strength and through our appropriate response to their needs, we build on their academic success.

U-STARS~PLUS teachers use ***TOPS*** folders (Coleman, Shah-Coltrane, & Harrison, 2010a, 2010b) to help them systematically observe their students. *TOPS* is a tool to help teachers recognize children (ages 5–9) who have outstanding potential and who may be gifted. In the development of the *TOPS*, specific attention was given to the recognition of educationally vulnerable children whose potential historically has been overlooked.

TOPS is designed to complement other sources of information used in a comprehensive approach to recognize children with outstanding potential. With *TOPS*, the teacher's knowledge of her or his students and the teacher's professional judgment are critical to the recognition of potential. *TOPS* helps a teacher make her or his observations more intentional, systematic, and purposeful so that the information can be used to provide more effective instruction.

TOPS is organized around nine domains:

1. Learns easily
2. Shows advanced skills
3. Displays curiosity and creativity
4. Has strong interests
5. Shows advanced reasoning and problem solving
6. Displays spatial abilities
7. Shows motivation
8. Shows social perceptiveness
9. Displays leadership

Several examples of behaviors that are indicators of potential are given for each domain. These behaviors capture both "teacher pleasing" and "non-teacher pleasing" behaviors, as bright children are not always "teacher-pleasers."

Using the *TOPS* Whole Class Observation Form (Coleman et al., 2010b), teachers initially observe their entire class to see which students seem to be showing signs of outstanding potential. They then follow up with observations of individual children to learn more if needed. The focus on children's strengths helps teachers reframe their thinking about educationally vulnerable children, reinforcing the at-potential mindset. The documentation of student strengths is used for instructional planning, communication with parents and other teachers, and eventually may serve as part of the evidence used to nominate a child for gifted education services.

The final element in this component is the building of a ***body of evidence*** that documents the child's strengths. This body of evidence allows us to look for patterns of strengths and needs so that we can plan for appropriate instruction. It helps us communicate with parents and others about the child by giving us concrete examples that show the child's strengths and needs. It also allows us to document student growth over time. The creation of a body of evidence further helps us when, and if, we decide to nominate a child for gifted education services. The use of a body of evidence to support formal identification mirrors best practices in gifted education by using multiple sources and types of information collected over multiple time periods (Coleman, 2003). The process of building a body of evidence is described in detail in the *U-STARS~PLUS Professional Development Kit* (Coleman & Shah-Coltrane, 2010b).

3. Hands-On, Inquiry-Based Science

The third component of *U-STARS~PLUS* is the use of hands-on, inquiry- based science. Science is the ideal platform to nurture, recognize, and respond to outstanding potential in young children (Shah-Coltrane & Coleman, 2005), and is especially helpful when we are looking for potential in children who will not be able to show us their strengths through language alone (Amaral, Garrison, & Klentschy, 2002; Carlson, 2000; Simon-Dudgeon & Egbert, 2001). Science that is inquiry-based and hands-on allows children to learn about their world with an emphasis on exploration and problem-solving (Basile, 1999; Donnellan & Roberts, 1985). Active learning differs from traditional expository methods that are dependent upon reading and writing. When children are "doing" science they have natural and authentic reasons to talk, read, write, and engage in mathematical thinking (Nyberg & McCloskey, 2008). In science, students have a chance to demonstrate their thinking and reasoning even before they have the words to fully express their understandings, and thus the words and language can be developed (Simon-Dudgeon & Egbert, 2001).

Science is also ideal because its rich problem-solving and exploratory approach allows us to recognize children's strengths as they tackle activities with no prelearned solutions. Further, science is the ideal content area to integrate reading, writing, math, and the arts (Royce & Wiley, 2005). When teachers observe their students using *TOPS* (Coleman et. al., 2010a, 2010b) during science explorations they are often able to recognize strengths in children who would be overlooked in other traditional school settings.

But, most of all, we chose science as the content for *U-STARS~PLUS* because it addresses children's natural curiosity and excitement about the world in which they live! The three elements that we focus on within this component are:

1. The use of science to promote thinking and to nurture achievement and language development.
2. The ability to actively captivate students' interest in real world settings while integrating the other content areas.
3. The use of hands-on, inquiry-based methods that allow children to learn through investigating as their vocabularies and skills continue to strengthen.

The science materials we have developed as a resource for teachers in *U-STARS~PLUS* materials are anchored in nationally accepted standards (National Science Education Standards, 1996). These materials are meant to help teachers expand and extend the science experiences they provide for their students. *U-STARS~PLUS* is not a science curriculum, but it is designed to complement whichever comprehensive science curriculum you use. The *U-STARS~PLUS Professional Development Kit* (Coleman & Shah-Coltrane, 2010b) includes additional information on best practices for teaching science to young children.

4. Family and School Partnerships

The fourth component of *U-STARS~PLUS* is family and school partnerships. The importance of family involvement in a child's school experience has been well documented (VanTassel-Baska, Patton, & Prillaman, 1991). The support system for the child is significantly strengthened when teachers and school personnel partner with families. When families are highly engaged in their child's education we see better school attendance, stronger academic performance, and a more positive school self-efficacy for the child (Cropper, 1998). The cornerstone of family involvement is a relationship built on trust, and often this trust must be earned over time. Educationally vulnerable children are the very ones who can benefit most from a strong family and school partnership. The *U-STARS~PLUS* approach includes four elements within the family and school partnership component: family engagement, effective parent/teacher conferences, family science packets, and cultural competence.

The first element is ***family involvement/engagement*** in the educational experiences with the child. Increasing family involvement in school-related activities cannot be left to chance. Our efforts must focus on building trust and on creating an inviting environment where families are welcomed and appreciated, and in which they can authentically participate in meaningful ways. This effort must be intentional and sustained so that the culture of the school is child and family-centered (Ritblatt, Beatty, Cronan, & Ochoa, 2002). Planning for a variety of ways and times that families can participate in school activities is helpful for families who are already juggling full lives.

Schools using *U-STARS~PLUS* adapt and strengthen their existing family involvement programs by incorporating science. When science is the focus we often see an increase in the involvement of fathers and siblings. The activities schools have used include family science nights, science carnivals, and science story nights, as well as the more traditional science fairs. Often the supplemental *U-STARS~PLUS* materials *Science & Literature Connections* and *Family Science Packets*, (Coleman & Shah-Coltrane, 2010a) are used as the base for these science events. Schools can increase attendance by including food, transportation (i.e., the school bus picks families up), and activities for siblings.

The second element of the family and school partnership component is ***effective parent/ teacher conferences and communication***. The *U-STARS~PLUS Professional Development Kit*

(Coleman & Shah-Coltrane, 2010b) offers several tips on increasing the communication at the conference through active listening and problem solving. When teachers use *TOPS* (Coleman, et. al., 2010a, 2010b) to document the child's strengths, their observations can serve as a focus for the conversations. In this way the teacher can share her insights on the child's strongest learning characteristics and can explain how these at-potential characteristics are being nurtured and responded to in the classroom. This approach also gives the parents an entry point for sharing their own observations and for suggesting additional ideas about how their child's strengths might be addressed. Using *TOPS* as a focus helps to ensure that the conference is effective and positive.

The third element of family involvement is the *U-STARS~PLUS* ***Family Science Packets.*** These materials are "science-in-a-bag" activities that children take home and complete with their families. Activities have been created to accompany major science topics covered in kindergarten through third grade. The *Family Science Packets* activities provide meaningful opportunities for families to engage in learning with their children. Each activity is designed to be completed in the home setting. The activities involve hands-on learning, guided experimentation, and discussion. Students collect and record observations as part of the experiments. The data sheets that have been completed at home are brought back to school so that the class can compile and analyze the data to see what was learned. The materials are family-friendly (Spanish translations are provided) and generate a high degree of family participation.

The fourth and final element in the family and school partnership component is ***cultural competence*** to help us better understand our students and their families (Villegas & Lucas, 2002). In this element we focus on the impact of poverty on children, on deepening our understanding of cultural/linguistic diversity, and on looking at the social and emotional needs of children (Wyner, Bridgeland, & Diiulio, 2009). These topics are addressed in the *U-STARS~PLUS* Professional Development Kit (Coleman & Shah-Coltrane, 2010b). By enhancing our cultural competence, we are better able to build relationships, increase communication, and expand opportunities for meaningful family involvement with all of our students' families.

5. Infrastructure Building for Systemic Change

The fifth component of the *U-STARS~PLUS* approach is different from the other four. Whereas the first four components focus on what the *U-STARS~PLUS* approach is and how it is implemented, the systemic change component focuses on creating the infrastructure to support and sustain the *U-STARS~PLUS* approach. Creating the infrastructure is a time-consuming activity, but it is absolutely essential to the success of any systemic change effort (Fixsen, Naoom, Blasé, Friedman, & Wallace, 2005). Implementing *U-STARS~PLUS* with sustainability in mind creates opportunities to build support for students, teachers, and schools, and thus enhances the ability of the district to nurture, recognize, and respond to students needs. The three elements of systemic change are capacity building, fidelity of implementation, and accountability.

The first element of systemic change is ***capacity building***. When we think about capacity for sustaining change we are referring to an infrastructure that includes people with knowledge and expertise, the allocation of resources (i.e., time, materials, and funds), and the intentional integration of new ideas within existing structures (Redding, 2009). Capacity building is critical at the classroom, school, and district levels. When we attend to capacity building from the beginning, we create the support needed to grow an initiative from the inside rather than having to rely on external supports for success (Fixsen et al., 2005). The primary vehicles to building capacity are professional development and policy.

Professional development must include teachers, principals, and other school personnel. The *U-STARS~PLUS Professional Development Kit* (Coleman & Shah-Coltrane, 2010b) is designed to be a part of an overall professional development initiative to support teachers in improving their ability to nurture, recognize, and respond to young children who have outstanding potential. Professional development is not a one-shot deal; it must be comprehensive and sustained (Winton et al., 2008). The best professional development is planned collaboratively with teachers, connects content and pedagogical skills, offers participatory activities, connects teacher and student learning, and is differentiated to meet individual teacher needs (Yore, Anderson, & Shymansky, 2005). Solid professional development is the linchpin to building ownership for change and creating an environment in which improvements can be self-sustaining. The *U-STARS~PLUS Professional Development Kit* offers a starting place for professional development planning.

The second vehicle needed for capacity building is policy development. Commitment to a new approach is established through its inclusion in policy. Policy guides the allocation of scarce resources to meet unlimited needs and determines who will get what resources and under what circumstance the resources/services will be delivered (Gallagher, 2006). Policy sets the expectations and ensures, to some extent, that new initiatives will be sustainable in spite of changes in personnel. In other words, policy helps to make sure that practices are not person-dependent and that the practice will continue despite the natural turnover we see in many of our schools.

Policy development takes place at many levels (i.e., classroom, school, school district, state, federal). With *U-STARS~PLUS* we can see policy changes at the classroom level if the teacher selects one or more of the component areas to include in her or his personal professional growth plan. School-level policy changes can be effected by intentionally embedding the primary components of *U-STARS~PLUS* (i.e., high-end learning opportunities, teachers' systematic observations, best practices in science, and family and school partnerships) in school improvement plans." At the district and state level, *U-STARS~PLUS* components can be built into policies related to gifted education, Title I initiatives, personnel preparation agendas, science curriculum initiatives, elementary education goals for reading and math, special education initiatives, parent engagement plans, and efforts aimed at closing the achievement gap. Although policy is not a guarantee of success, it is critical for the sustainability of any effort. Thinking about how the *U-STARS~PLUS* approach fits within existing policies is essential to ensure sustainability. Policy at the state and federal level is reflected in laws that guide identification and services for children with high potential.

The second element of systemic change is ***fidelity of implementation***, the extent to which an approach is implemented as it was intended or designed. *U-STARS~PLUS* fidelity of implementation rubrics for classroom, school, and district levels describe (see Tables 2–4) *U-STARS~PLUS* from emerging and developing to proficient and optimal implementation. The rubrics clarify expected outcomes, communicate intent, and can serve as a base for self-reflection as well as a marker for accountability. The major uses of the fidelity rubrics include exploring current needs, planning for the future, and providing baseline information that can document growth.

Because *U-STARS~PLUS* is an approach designed to be implemented in a variety of settings, there must always be a degree of flexibility built into fidelity. The flexibility is built around "anchor" areas that help to maintain the integrity of the implementation. This flexibility allows the *U-STARS~PLUS* approach to work within a specific setting. For example, *U-STARS~PLUS*

- Can fit well with different science curriculums as long as the curriculum is standards-based and emphasizes hands-on, inquiry-based methods,
- Can be implemented in urban and rural schools as long as the infrastructure is built to support implementation, and
- Can fit well with other initiatives across the curriculum (e.g., reading approaches, technology plans, and parent/community involvement efforts).

The fidelity of implementation rubrics can help to guide decision making and accountability for providing resources and support needed to implement *U-STARS~PLUS* successfully.

The final element within systemic change is the need for measures of ***accountability***. The first level of accountability focuses on the school district and school to assure that if appropriate support for implementing *U-STARS~PLUS* has been provided (the district and school fidelity of implementation rubrics can guide these reviews). The second level of accountability addresses teachers and their ability to put into practice the *U-STARS~PLUS* components. (This is guided by the classroom fidelity of implementation rubric.)

Once we have confidence that the district and school supports have been provided and that teachers are putting the ideas into practice in their classrooms, we can focus on the impact *U-STARS~PLUS* has on students. Each district and school will have its own approach to looking at performance at these levels, but we strongly encourage including some accountability measures at each level.

Table 2. *U-STARS~PLUS* FIDELITY of IMPLEMENTATION: CLASSROOM RUBRIC

Critical Components	Not Evident	Emerging	Developing	Proficient	Optimal
Teacher's Observation of Potential in Students (TOPS) • Supports "at-potential" view of all students. • Recognizes students with outstanding potential, in particularly those from educationally vulnerable populations. • Informs teachers about student strengths and needs. • Informs classroom instruction and academic service options. • Provides information from a variety of settings, over time. • Supports conferencing with teachers, parents, and students. • Informs services and supports for students for the following year. • Informs a body-of-evidence. • Leads to referrals for Gifted and Talented program services. • Integrates with school policies and Gifted and Talented program practices.	*TOPS* is not being used.	• Beginning evidence of understanding of theoretical background and practical application of *TOPS*. • Used for a few students, sporadically. • Completed in one sitting or in retrospect.	• Use of *TOPS* on a regular basis, beginning with the whole-class observation which leads to some individual observations. • Experimenting with guiding classroom instruction and sharing students' strengths and needs.	• Consistent integration of *TOPS* for student observations. • Entire observation process followed; students with outstanding potential are recognized • Information from observations are used to plan appropriate response for students' strengths and needs.	• Significant and intentional use in classroom to see high potential in students, including those from educationally vulnerable populations. • Seamless use to guide classroom instruction, share student strengths and needs with other teachers, and communicate with families. • Use as a base for creating a body of evidence to document the child's strengths and needs. • Helps to guide Gifted and Talented referrals, placement and services in and out of the general education classroom, and policy issues.
Classroom Differentiation • Responds to strengths and needs of students. • Relies on dynamic assessment to inform instruction, including progress monitoring and self-assessment. • Includes differentiation strategies: compacting, tiering, centers, independent studies/small group contracts, effective questioning. • Varies based on readiness, interest, strengths, and needs. • Uses student-centered, open-ended, product choice. • Uses a variety of materials and resources for student use. • Leads to flexible grouping. • Uses *U-STARS~PLUS* materials.	Classroom differentiation is not being used.	• Beginning evidence of understanding of theoretical background and practical application of differentiation. • Few activities support appropriate challenge and interest for students at different levels.	• Better understanding of the theoretical background. • Some application in the classroom on a regular basis. • Experimenting with ideas in a variety of ways and settings	• Consistent integration of high-end learning opportunities in the classroom. • Evident in student work, curriculum planning, and classroom instruction. • Used to create an optimal learning environment, which nurtures and responds to potential.	• Used to create an optimal learning environment, which nurtures and responds to potential. • Clearly evident in assessment, student work, planning, and instruction. • Challenging and meaningful work consistently facilitated for all students, seamlessly

Table 2. *U-STARS~PLUS* FIDELITY of IMPLEMENTATION: CLASSROOM RUBRIC (cont'd)

Critical Components	Not Evident	Emerging	Developing	Proficient	Optimal
Hands-On, Inquiry-Based Science • Provides hands-on activities and explorations. • Supports inquiry-rich learning, students follow own questions and experiment. • Integrates with other subject areas. • Fosters authentic learning, using natural environments. • Uses a variety of materials and resources available. • Responds to students' curiosity and interests. • Leads to scientific understanding and realities. • Includes long-term projects; data collections and analysis. • Incorporates student-centered; teacher guided.	Hands-on, inquiry-based science is not being facilitated	• Beginning evidence of understanding of theoretical background and practical application of hands-on, inquiry-based science. • Few activities done in isolation; more hands-on than inquiry; does involve students.	• Some Some integration of hands-on activities on a regular basis in the classroom. • Experimenting with inquiry-based explorations in a variety of ways and settings. • Better understanding of the theoretical background.	• Consistent integration of hands-on, inquiry-based science opportunities in the classroom. • Student interest and curiosity are considered. • Evident in student work, curriculum planning, and classroom instruction. • Used to nurture and respond to outstanding potential.	• Significant and intentional integration of hands-on, inquiry-based science, where appropriate. • Classroom environment clearly supports inquiry-based learning leading to scientific understanding. • Clearly evident in assessment, student work, planning, and curriculum and instruction. • Leads to better understanding of students' potential.
Family Involvement • Considers diversity of family backgrounds (race/ethnicity, socio-economic, cultural/linguistic, and others) in all aspects, including communication, events, and academic issues. • Uses regular and varied forms of communication. • Includes a variety of ways to involve families in the classroom, including academic, policy, social/emotional focused. • Provides opportunities for family-led initiatives.	Family involvement specific to U-STARS~PLUS is not occurring	• Beginning evidence of understanding and theoretical background and practical application of family involvement. • Occasional family involvement activities take place. • Beginning to learn about families and backgrounds.	• Some family involvement activities take place on a regular basis. • Involvement concentrates on student and family needs. • Experimenting with family involvement in new ways to incorporate science.	• Consistent effort is given to integrate families into school and classroom. • Family needs are considered. • Regular and varied communication with families. • Variety of family involvement opportunities are available; some family-centered.	• All families are intentionally involved in meaningful aspects of the classroom. • Integration of family involvement into the academic areas of their children. • Family-led initiatives are intentionally encouraged and take place in the classroom. • Family involvement leads to better understanding of families and students.

Table 3. *U-STARS~PLUS* FIDELITY of IMPLEMENTATION: SCHOOL RUBRIC

Critical Components	Not Evident	Emerging	Developing	Proficient	Optimal
Implementation Teams • Includes a core team and other participating teachers (e.g., K–3 and others, as appropriate). • Communicates and collaborates with other stakeholders. • Facilitates implementation; uses Implementation Plan as guide. • Understands *U-STARS~PLUS.* • Attends professional development experiences, on- and off-site. • Helps to set the pace and guide progress. • Recruits others to be involved; involves a variety of stakeholders.	Implementation is not established.	• Team composition is beginning to form, partially represented by K–3 teachers and others. • Team members acknowledge responsibility for implementation. • Beginning evidence of understanding theoretical background and application of *U-STARS~PLUS.*	• Team meets occasionally for specific purposes. • Core team members have attended professional activities connected to U-STARS~PLUS. • Experimenting with facilitating implementation.	• Implementation team composition is fully established and represented. • Team consistently facilitates implementation of *U-STARS~PLUS.* • All team members have a firm understanding of *U-STARS-PLUS* and have attended professional development.	• Team is composed of all major stakeholders appropriate for the school, including parents. • Team seamlessly integrates implementation of *U-STARS~PLUS* in major aspects of school, where appropriate. • Team communicates meaningful progress with appropriate audiences. • Team has significant knowledge of U-STARS~PLUS and adapts model to meet own needs.
Implementation Plan The Implementation Plan addresses the following key components: • Focus areas: high-end learning opportunities, teachers' systematic observations/*TOPS*, hands-on inquiry-based science, family involvement • Action plan: timeline, resources, professional development, supports/needs • Incorporates feedback from fidelity of implementation reviews and other reflections	Plan is not complete at this time.	• Planning has started, beginning conversations are occurring. • Ideas and focus of action plans are being discussed.	• Plan outlines some key components for implementation of focus areas. • Experimenting with incorporation of fidelity of implementation as a guide for implementation.	• Plan provides a framework and guidelines for consistent use of *U-STARS~PLUS.* • Integration of fidelity of implementation review for planning. • Includes all plan components.	• Plan is fully integrated into all school policies and procedures and is part of the overall school plan. • Plan outlines ways that *U-STARS~PLUS* is growing and affects programs schoolwide. • Long-range goals are clearly evident. • Fidelity of implementation intentionally guides progress.

Table 3. *U-STARS~PLUS* FIDELITY of IMPLEMENTATION: SCHOOL RUBRIC (cont'd)

Critical Components	Not Evident	Emerging	Developing	Proficient	Optimal
Schoolwide Integration • Aligns with and extends curriculum and instruction. • Supports general education. • Aligns with and extends other education programs, (e.g., Gifted and Talented and Eearly Childhood programs). • Integrates with policy and procedures. • Includes appropriate resources and support.	No integration is evident at this time.	• Beginning evidence of schoolwide integration. • Occasional connections have been made with other areas across the school.	• Some schoolwide integration is evident on a regular basis. • Some resources and support are evident in curriculum and instruction. • Experimenting with new ways to integrate *U-STARS~PLUS* across the school.	• Schoolwide integration is evident in many areas of curriculum and instruction; policies and procedures. • Consistent support is evident for students and teachers. • Many resources exist for schoolwide integration.	• Seamless schoolwide integration of *U-STARS~PLUS* throughout curriculum and instruction, policies and procedures, and resources. • Systematic approaches to address students recognized with outstanding potential are schoolwide. • Continuous professional development opportunities are available.
Family Involvement • Considers diversity of family backgrounds (race/ethnicity, socioeconomic, cultural/linguistic, and others) in all aspects of school, including communication, events, and academic issues. • Focuses on involvement in schoolwide activities (e.g., academic, social, and empowering ways) • Provides and encourages leadership opportunities for parents.	No activities are planned to encourage family involvement in relation to *U-STARS~PLUS*.	• Beginning School provides occasional opportunities for family involvement through *U-STARS~PLUS*. • Participation of families is minimal in the school.	• School provides some opportunities for family involvement on a regular basis. • Parents assume some leadership roles and participate on a regular basis. • School experiments with new ways to address the needs of diverse families.	• Schoolwide opportunities for family involvement are consistently available. • Inclusive opportunities are offered to promote involvement of all families. • Parents are consistently involved in planning and implementing schoolwide activities.	• Initiatives are established to intentionally and meaningfully involve all families. • Seamless integration of family involvement in meaningful aspects of the school. • Family involvement activities are well supported and attended. • Parents have leadership roles in a variety of aspects of school. • All families are intentionally involved in meaningful aspects of the school.

Table 4. *U-STARS~PLUS* FIDELITY of IMPLEMENTATION: DISTRICT RUBRIC

Critical Components	Not Evident	Emerging	Developing	Proficient	Optimal
Coordination of District Implementation • Addresses team membership. • Facilitates information sharing. • Develops implementation plans. • Includes active use of materials. • Plans for growth within district. • Includes professional development. • Plans for districtwide integration with other programs. • Fosters widespread "buy-in."	No coordination of *U-STARS ~PLUS* at district level.	• Beginning coordination of *U-STARS~PLUS* schools, including professional development, materials, overall implementation. • Information is being shared across schools. • Basic professional development is encouraged.	• Some integration and alignment of *U-STARS~PLUS* among schools and within district initiatives. • Initial plans for growing *U-STARS ~PLUS* are developed. • District shows support for schools' implementation plans.	• Consistent integration and alignment of *U-STARS~PLUS* within schools and within district initiatives. • District shows strong support for school implementation plans and Fidelity of Implementation. • Interest in *U-STARS~PLUS* is encouraged.	• Meaningful integration of *U-STARS~PLUS* where appropriate throughout the district. • *U-STARS~PLUS* schools are clearly and significantly supported. • *U-STARS~PLUS* is a priority for the district staff and this is clearly evident to the schools.
Interactions With *U-STARS~PLUS* Schools • Initiates contact with *U-STARS~PLUS* schools (via phone, e-mail, and/or in person) about implementation and integration of *U-STARS~PLUS* within district. • Facilitates collaborative information gathering and sharing across schools. • Facilitates interaction in a variety of settings, on- and off-site. • Participates in *U-STARS~PLUS* activities.	No interactions with *U-STARS~ PLUS* schools occur.	• *U-STARS~PLUS* contact within district is intermittent. • Information sharing is accomplished occasionally.	• Some regular contact across the district *U-STARS~ PLUS* schools occurs. • Information sharing across schools occurs somewhat.	• Regular, collaborative contact among the *U-STARS~PLUS* schools occurs. • Evident collaboration gathering and sharing information.	• Intentional and meaningful contact and communication among the *U-STARS~PLUS* schools. • Meaningful interaction and communication across schools and district.

Table 4. *U-STARS~PLUS* FIDELITY of IMPLEMENTATION: DISTRICT RUBRIC (cont'd)

Critical Components	Not Evident	Emerging	Developing	Proficient	Optimal
Communication • Fosters communication within district and beyond, including school board, parents, community, and local, state, and national audiences. • Establishes connections between and among schools. • Celebrates successes of program • Acts as "*U-STARS~PLUS* Ambassador."	No communication about *U-STARS~PLUS* at district level.	• Beginning evidence of schoolwide integration. • Occasional connections have been made with other areas across the school.	• Communication strategies within district are established and functioning. • Some *U-STARS~PLUS* activities and positive aspects/ideas are being shared.	• Regular sharing and celebration of project information and successes. • Clear and consistent connections throughout district are sustained. • Experimenting with role as "*U-STARS~PLUS* Ambassador" to a wider audience.	• Significant and meaningful sharing of information to all involved audiences. • Ambassadorship clearly evident on *U-STARS~PLUS* at all levels. • Communication among schools, facilitated by district, is significant and meaningful. •
Resources and Support • Provides for fiscal support • Seeking out additional resources/funding opportunities • Funds set aside specifically for purchase of *U-STARS~PLUS* materials and professional development from existing budgets. • Develops human expertise adequate personnel available to support *U-STARS~PLUS* methods and materials • substitute personnel available so teachers can attend staff development support for leadership. • Facilitates time for staff development, planning, integration. • Addresses policies within the district.	No additional resources and support are allocated for *U-STARS~PLUS*.	• Few resources are available for *U-STARS~PLUS* professional development, materials, supplies, and staff.	• Some resources are available for *U-STARS~PLUS* professional development, materials, supplies, and staff.	• Many resources are available for *U-STARS~PLUS* professional development, materials, supplies, and staff. • Plans for ensuring future availability are underway. • District policies have been reviewed with *U-STARS~PLUS* involved.	• Extensive resources and support for *U-STARS~PLUS* are committed and strategically used. • Significant integration of resources and support for *U-STARS~PLUS* schools have been allocated. • Policies have been revised and created to facilitate *U-STARS~PLUS*.

The Magic of Synergy

Although each of the five *U-STARS~PLUS* components (i.e., high-end learning opportunities, teachers' systematic observations of potential, hands-on/inquiry-based science, family and school partnerships, and infrastructure for systemic change) can be used in isolation, the real benefit comes when we implement these components together. The relationships among the components are such that when they are used in concert, the effect of each is strengthened. The true power and magic of this approach happens when all five components work together.

High-end learning environments create opportunities for us to see children tackling, wrestling with, and mastering challenging content. If we are intentionally watching for our students' strengths using *TOPS* and if we have created high-end learning environments, we are more likely to see these indicators of potential. When we add hands-on, inquiry-based science to this mix we can better recognize the abilities of children who will show their strengths in areas that are not heavily language-dependent.

When we use the *TOPS* to document the strengths of our students we can connect this information back to instructional planning to meet students' needs and we can share our insights during parent conferences focusing on a child's strengths. This focus on a child's strengths during parent conferences, combined with the *Family Science Packets*, brings teachers and parents together in a shared positive view of the child's academic potential. This shared positive view builds trusting relationships between the family and the school personnel.

When implementation is supported (through personnel preparation, policy development, and resource allocation), the capacity for excellence at the district, school, and classroom levels increases. This capacity building further energizes the process of implementation and sets the stage for the sustainability necessary to make a difference in the lives of our most educationally vulnerable children. Through these efforts we begin to see how the educational culture can change from one of "at risk" to one of "at potential" for all of the children we teach. With this focus and with the strong relationships with parents we can help make every child's school experience positive, engaging, and successful.

So, although each of the five components of *U-STARS~PLUS* can be implemented in isolation, the star will shine more brightly when all five points are activated!

Getting Started Questions

- How does the philosophy of *U–STARS~PLUS* fit with your current beliefs?
- What are you already doing at the classroom, school, and district levels that fit with the five *U–STARS~PLUS* components (i.e., high-end learning; teacher observation of potential; science inquiry; family involvement; systemic change)?
- What would the benefits be for teachers, parents, and children if you adopt the *U–STARS~PLUS* approach?
- What challenges will you face if you adopt the *U–STARS~PLUS* approach and how can you overcome these challenges?

References

Allington, R. L. (2002, June). What I've learned about effective reading instruction: From a decade of studying exemplary elementary classroom teachers. *Phi Delta Kappan, 83*, 740.

Amaral, O. M., Garrison, L., & Klentschy, M. (2002). Helping English learners increase achievement through inquiry-based science instruction. *Bilingual Research Journal, 26*, 214–239.

Barbarin, O. A. (2002). Culture and ethnicity in social, emotional and academic development. *The Kauffman Early Education Exchange, 1*(1), 45–61.

Basile, C. G. (1999, September). Collecting data outdoors: Making connections to the real world. *Teaching Children Mathematics, 6*(1), 8–11.

Bjork, J. (2005). Teaching through trade books: From sap to syrup. *Science & Children, 43*(3), 16–18.

Bloom, B. Samuel., Krathwohl, D. R., & Masia, B. B. (1956). *Taxonomy of educational objectives: The classification of educational goals*. New York, NY: Longmans Green.

Briggs, C. J., Reis, S. M., & Sullivan, E. E. (2008). A national view of promising programs and practices for culturally, linguistically, and ethnically diverse gifted and talented students. *Gifted Child Quarterly, 52*, 131–145.

Burchinal, M. R., Peisner-Feinberg, E., Pianta, R., & Howes, C. (2002). Development of academic skills from preschool through second grade: Family and classroom predictors of developmental trajectories. *Journal of School Psychology, 40*, 415–436.

Carlson, C. (2000). Scientific literacy for all. *Science Teacher, 76*(3), 48–52.

Carnegie-IAS. (2009). The opportunity equation: Transforming mathematics and science education for citizenship and the global economy. Retrieved from http://www.opportunityequation.org/report/urgency-opportunity/

Cheong, W. (2000, March/April). The power of questioning. *Connect, 9–10*. Retrieved from http://bonfire.learn.unc.edu/zoo/03_info/cheong_reading.pdf

Cherry, L. (2006). Trade books for learning: An author's view. *Science & Children, 44*(3), 44–47.

Coleman, M. R. (1994). Using cooperative learning with gifted students. *Gifted Child Today, 17*(6), 36–38.

Coleman, M. R. (1996). How to reward achievement: Creating individualized learning experiences. *Gifted Child Today, 19*(5), 48–49.

Coleman, M. R. (1998). Are we serious about meeting student needs? *Gifted Child Today, 21*(1), 40–41.

Coleman, M. R. (2000). Back to the future. *Gifted Child Today, 22*(6), 16–18.

Coleman, M. R. (2003). Four variables for success. *Gifted Child Today, 26*(1), 22–24.

Coleman, M. R. (2005). Cooperative learning and gifted learners. In F. A. Karnes & S. M. Bean (Eds.), *Methods and materials for teaching the gifted* (pp. 519–542). Waco, TX: Prufrock Press.

Coleman, M. R., & Shah-Coltrane, S. (2010a). *U-STARS~PLUS family science packets*. Arlington, VA: Council for Exceptional Children.

Coleman, M. R., & Shah-Coltrane, S. (2010b). *U-STARS~PLUS professional development kit*. Arlington, VA: Council for Exceptional Children.

Coleman, M.R., Shah-Coltrane, S., & Harrison, A. (2010a). *Teacher's observation of potential in students: Individual student form*. Arlington, VA: Council for Exceptional Children.

Coleman, M.R., Shah-Coltrane, S., & Harrison, A. (2010b). *Teacher's observation of potential in students: Whole class form*. Arlington, VA: Council for Exceptional Children.

Cropper, C. (1998). Fostering parental involvement in the education of the gifted minority student. *Gifted Child Today, 21*(1), 20–24.

Donnellan, K., & Roberts, G. (1985, January). What research says: Activity-based elementary science: A double bonus. *Science & Children, 22*(4), 119–121.

Fixsen, D. L., Naoom, S. F., Blasé, K. A., Friedman, R. M., & Wallace, F. (2005). *Implementation research: A synthesis of the literature*. Unpublished manuscript. Gainesville, FL: University of Florida National Implementation Research Network.

Ford, D. J. (2004). Scaffolding preservice teachers' evaluation of children's science literature. Attention to science-focused genres and use. *Journal of Science Teacher Education, 15*, 133–153.

Ford, D. Y., & Grantham, T. C. (2003). Providing access for culturally diverse gifted students: From deficit to dynamic thinking. *Theory Into Practice, 42*, 217–225.

Ford, D. Y., & Harmon, D. A. (2001). Equity and excellence: Providing access to gifted education for culturally diverse students. *Journal of Secondary Gifted Education, 12*, 141–147.

Ford, D. Y., Moore, J. L. III., & Milner, H. R. (2005). Beyond colorblindness: A model of culture with implications for gifted education. *Roeper Review, 27*, 97–103.

Gall, M. (1984). Synthesis of research on teacher's questioning. *Educational Leadership, 42*(3), 40–47.

Gallagher, J. (2006). *Driving changes in special education*. Baltimore, MD: Brookes.

Gandara, P. (2005). *Fragile futures: Risk and vulnerability among Latino high achievers*. Princeton, NJ: Educational Testing Service.

Hertzog, N. (2005). Equity and access: Creating general education classrooms responsive to potential giftedness. *Journal for the Education of the Gifted, 29*, 213–257.

Jensen, E. (2009). *Teaching with poverty in mind*. Alexandria, VA: Association of Supervision and Curriculum Development.

Kirk, S., Gallagher, J., Coleman, M., & Anastasiow, N. (2009). *Educating exceptional children* (12th ed.) Boston, MA: Houghton Mifflin.

Kirschenbaum, R. J. (1998). Dynamic assessment and its use with underserved gifted and talented populations. *Gifted Child Quarterly, 42*, 140–147.

Monhardt, L., & Monhardt, R. (2006). Creating a context for the learning of science process skills through picture books. *Early Childhood Education Journal, 34*, 66–71.

National Research Council. (2002). *Minority students in special and gifted education*. Washington, DC: National Academies Press.

National Science Education Standards. (1996). *Science content standards.* Retrieved from www.nap.edu

Nyberg, L., & McCloskey, S. (2008). Integration with integrity. *Science & Children, 46*(3), 46–49.

Olszewski-Kubilius, P., Lee, S., Ngoi, M., & Ngoi, D. (2004). Addressing the achievement gap between minority and nonminority children by increasing access to gifted programs. *Journal for the Education of the Gifted, 28*, 127–158.

Redding, S. (2009). *Framework for an effective statewide system of support*. Lincoln, IL: Center on Innovation and Improvement.

Ritblatt, W., Beatty, J., Cronan, T., & Ochoa, A. (2002). Relationships among perceptions of parent involvement, time allocation, and demographic characteristics: Implication for policy formation. *Journal of Community Psychology, 30*, 519–545.

Royce, C. A., & Wiley, D. A. (2005). The common ground: A rationale for integrating science and reading. *Science & Children*, *42*(5), 40–42. Retrieved from http://www.nsta.org/publications/news/story.aspx?id=50210&print=true

Rubie-Davies, C. M. (2007). Classroom interactions: Exploring the practices of high and low expectation teachers. *British Journal of Educational Psychology*, 77, 289–306.

Shah-Coltrane, S. S., & Coleman, M. R. (2005, Fall/Winter). Using science as a vehicle: Search for outstanding potential in underserved populations. *Gifted Education Communicator, 36*(3–4), 20–23.

Simon-Dudgeon, C., & Egbert, J. (2001). Science as a second language: Verbal interactive strategies help English language learners develop academic vocabulary. *Science Teacher, 67*(3), 28–32.

Tomlinson, C. A., Ford, D. Y., Reis, S. M., Briggs, C. J., & Strickland, C. A. (2004). *In search of the dream: Designing schools and classrooms that work for high potential students from diverse cultural backgrounds*. Washington, DC: National Association for Gifted Children.

VanTassel-Baska, J., Patton, J., & Prillaman, D. (1991). *Gifted youth at risk: A report of a national study*. Reston, VA: Council for Exceptional Children.

Villegas, A. M., & Lucas, T. (2002). Preparing culturally responsive teachers: Rethinking the curriculum. *Journal of Teacher Education, 53*, 20–32.

Winton, P. J., McCollum, J. A., & Catlett, C. (2008). A framework and recommendation for a cross-agency professional development system. In P. J. Winton, J. A. McCollum, & C. Catlett (Eds.), *Practical approaches to early childhood professional development* (pp. 263–272). Washington, DC: Zero to Three National Center for Infants, Toddlers, and Families.

Wyner, J. S., Bridgeland, J. M., & Diiulio, J. J. (2009). *Achievementrap: How America is failing millions of high-achieving students from lower-income families*. A report from the Jack Kent Cooke Foundation. Retrieved from www.jkcf.org/assets/files/0000/0084/Achievement_Trap.pdf

Yore, L. D., Anderson, J. O., & Shymansky, J. A. (2005). Sensing the impact of elementary school science reform: A study of stakeholder perceptions of implementation, constructivist strategies, and school-home collaboration. *Journal of Science Teacher Education, 16*, 65–88.

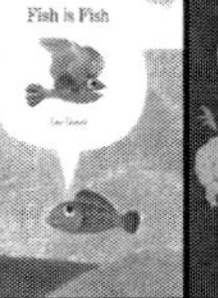

U-STARS~PLUS

Science & Literature Connections

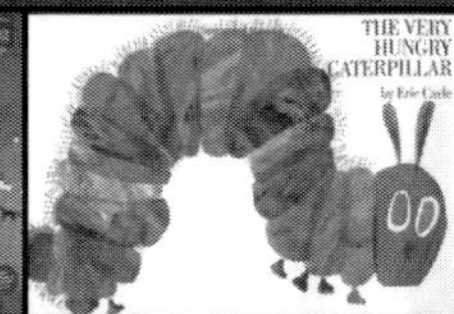

U-STARS~PLUS

Science & Literature Connections

(continued)

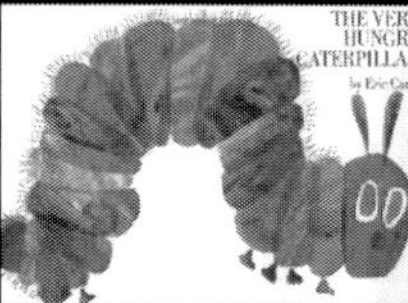

Alexander and the Wind-Up Mouse

Written and Illustrated by: Leo Lionni
Published by: Dragonfly Books

Major Topics:

Living and Non-Living Things
Organisms – Animals, Basic Needs, Behavior

National Science Education Content Standards (1996)

Life Science

- The Characteristics of Organisms
- Organisms and Their Environments

Science and Technology

- Abilities to Distinguish Between Natural Objects and Objects Designed by Humans

Summary:

Alexander, a real living mouse, spends his days scurrying around his home searching for food and avoiding danger. One day, he comes across a mouse of a different sort—a wind-up toy mouse named Willy. Alexander is surprised to find out that the people living in the house love Willy, but they do not like him. Although Willy can only move about when he is wound up with a key, he and Alexander become friends. Alexander begins to envy Willy's life as a toy mouse until Willy ends up in a "toy discard" box. Alexander then works to have Willy changed into a living mouse, like himself.

Science Concept Map

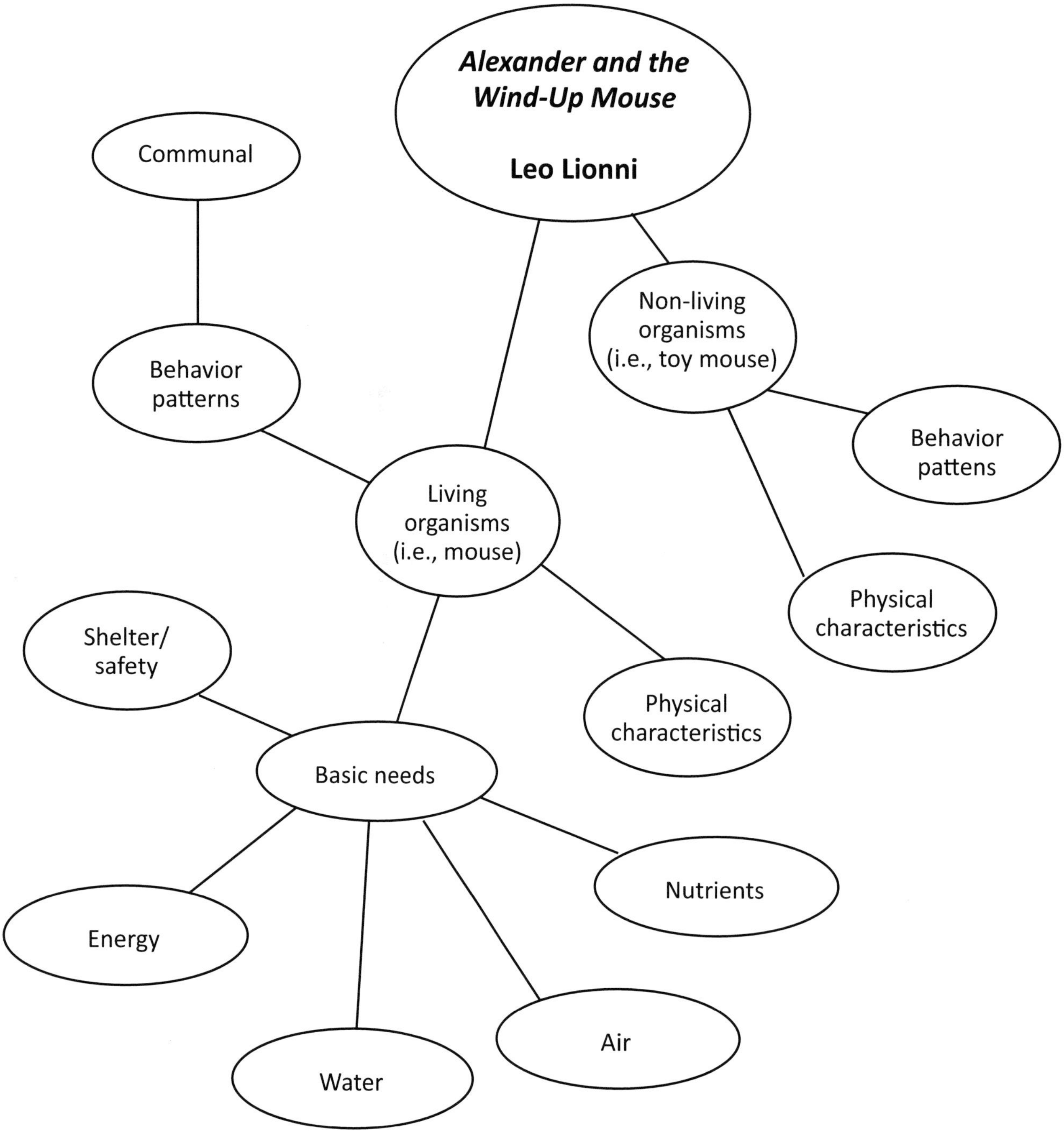

Alexander and the Wind-Up Mouse

Leo Lionni

Communal

Behavior patterns

Living organisms (i.e., mouse)

Non-living organisms (i.e., toy mouse)

Behavior pattens

Physical characteristics

Shelter/ safety

Physical characteristics

Basic needs

Nutrients

Energy

Air

Water

Thinking Questions Based on Bloom's Taxonomy: *Alexander and the Wind-Up Mouse*

1. **Knowledge:**
   What did the people in the house do when they saw Alexander? What types of things did Alexander do inside the house? Did the people in the house like Alexander? What was Willy the Mouse? What happened to Willy? Did the people in the house like Willy? Did Alexander ever become a toy mouse?

2. **Comprehension:**
   How did the people in the house treat Willy and Alexander differently? Why did the people not like Alexander? Why did the people like Willy? Why did Alexander like Willy? Explain what types of things toy Willy needed to survive. Explain what types of things Alexander needed to survive. Why did Alexander want to be a non-living toy mouse like Willy?

3. **Application:**
   In your own home, do you have animals or toys that you like and don't like? Why do you like them? Why do you not like them? Mice are communal animals, meaning they like to belong to a community or group of mice. Give examples of the kinds of groups to which you belong. What needs do the groups meet for you?

4. **Analysis:**
   Compare and contrast Alexander and Willy. How were they alike and different physically? How were their needs alike and different? Determine characteristics of living and non-living things. If Alexander became a toy like Willy, predict what would have happened to him. How did the people treat Alexander and Willy?

5. **Synthesis:**
   Pretend you have a real living pet. What would you need to do in order to take care of your pet? What kinds of things does your family do to take care of you? How do you take care of yourself? Tell about a time when you felt that you didn't belong and wanted to be someone else like Alexander. At the end, why did Alexander change his mind and instead have Willy become a living mouse?

6. **Evaluation:**
   The people living in the house tried to get rid of Alexander. What would you do if you had a mouse in your house? Explain. Would you rather be a real mouse or a toy mouse? Justify your answer. In your opinion, was it a good or bad choice for Alexander to have Willy changed to a real living mouse?

Follow-Up Activities

Alexander and the Wind-Up Mouse

- Create a visual project categorizing living and non-living things. Use magazine pictures, words, student-created artwork, and so forth. Have students justify their choices.

- Observe animals in the classroom, in and around school, and in the community. Determine their basic needs. How do animals survive in man-made habitats? In natural habitats?

- Conduct experiments with plants to learn about the basic needs of organisms. Grow several plants with different variables, possibly limiting each to one basic need (i.e., water, nutrients, light). Compare the plants in the experiment to one which receives all the basic needs.

- Compare and contrast various natural habitats versus man-made habitats. How do each meet the needs of its inhabitants? Consider plants and animals.

- Talk to students about personal needs and wants. How do family and community help them meet their needs? Develop a creative piece of literature, song, poem, and so forth that conveys needs/wants and how the world around the students supports them.

- Research other specific interests, curiosities, and basic information about animals, basic needs of organisms, and living and non-living things. Provide and encourage the use of multiple sources of information. Have students share their learning in a variety of ways.

Bringing the Rain to Kapiti Plain

Written by: Verna Aardema
Published by: Penguin Young Readers Group

Major Topics:

Environment – Interdependency, Changes
Organisms – Animals, Plants, Basic Needs, Behavior, Habitats
Weather – Rain, Drought, Environment Changes

National Science Education Content Standards (1996)

Life Science

- The Characteristics of Organisms
- Organisms and Their Environments

Earth and Space Science

- Changes in the Earth and Sky
- Objects in the Sky

Science in Personal and Social Perspectives

- Types of Resources
- Changes in the Environment

Summary:

This Nandi tale explains the importance of rain to the survival of the Kapiti Plain in Africa. One year, the rains are long overdue. The Kapiti Plain is dry and the grass has turned brown and dead — leaving the animals hungry and dry. Ki-pat, the herdsman, is watching his herd as a big cloud heavy with rain looms overhead. Ki-pat creates an arrow from an eagle feather and pierces the cloud releasing the much needed rain onto Kapiti Plain. The rain revives the Kapiti Plain including the grass, the animals, and the people. They all thrive as the Kapiti Plain rebalances.

Science Concept Map

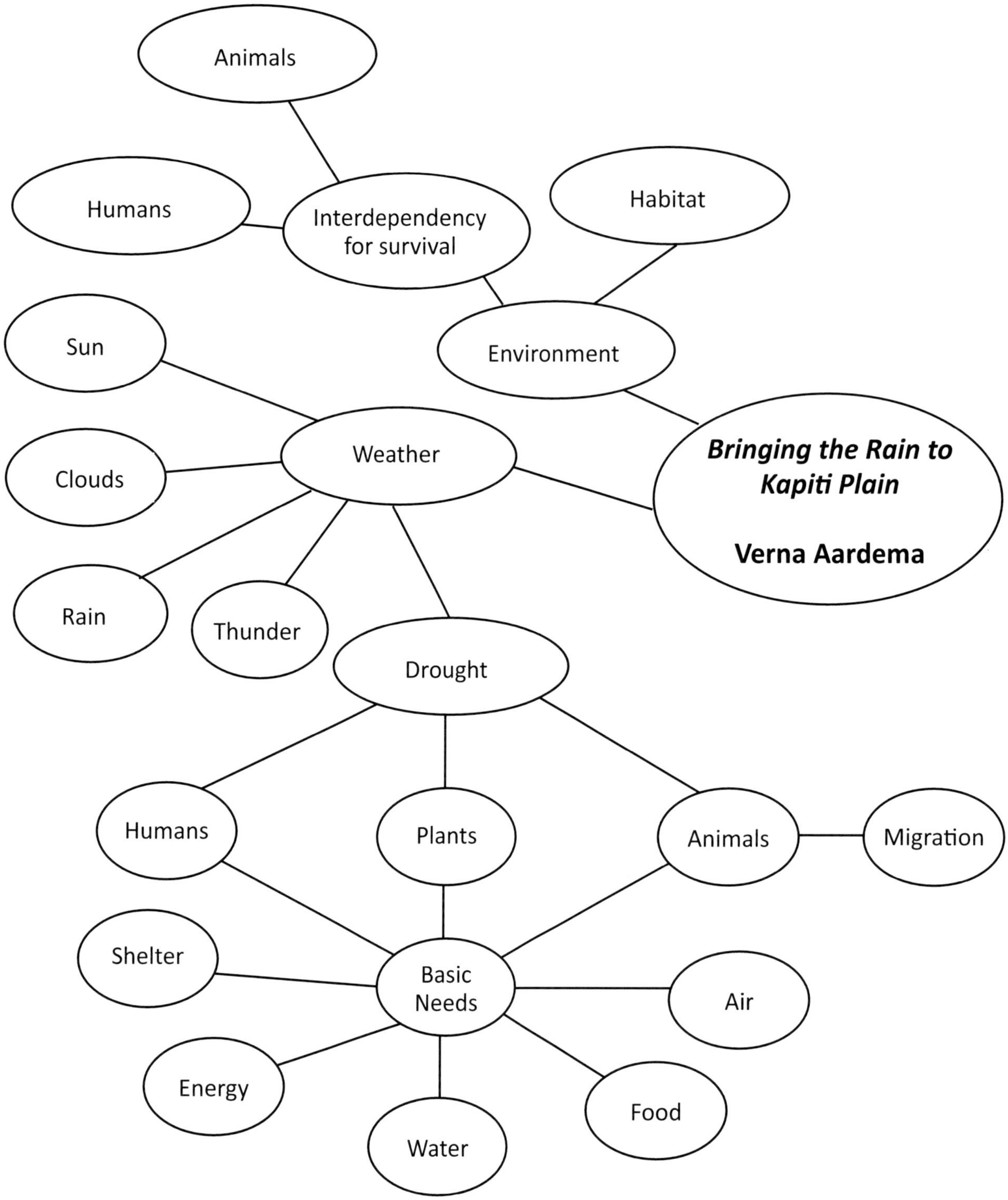

Thinking Questions Based on Bloom's Taxonomy: *Bringing the Rain to Kapiti Plain*

1. **Knowledge:**
Where does this story take place? What lives in the Kapiti Plain? What was the problem in the story? Who solves the problem? What was affected by the drought? What resources did Ki-pat use to make his arrow?

2. **Comprehension:**
Explain why the animals had started to migrate from the Kapiti Plain. Describe the characteristics of an African plain. How does Ki-pat solve the problem in the story? How did piercing the cloud help the Kapiti Plain? Why is rain important to the Kapiti Plain?

3. **Application:**
In this story, there is a dark, heavy cloud covering the Kapiti Plain. What does seeing this cloud predict about the weather? Give examples of other ways you know rain and other types of weather are coming. Predict how your life would be different if there was a drought in your community. How would you and the local environment be affected?

4. **Analysis:**
Compare and contrast the Kapiti Plain during the drought and after the rain (consider the animals and plants of the Plain). Ki-pat pierced the cloud with an arrow to cause the rain to fall. Is this really how it rains? Explain. Compare and contrast the Kapiti Plain with where you live. How does each habitat meet the needs of its inhabitants?

5. **Synthesis:**
Explain the interdependency of the plants, people, and animals of the Kapiti Plain. Determine what would happen if the drought continued. Rain was critical to the survival of the Kapiti Plain. How is rain important to you and where you live? How are rain and the water cycle important for the survival of all living things? How do other types of weather affect your daily life?

6. **Evaluation:**
In your opinion, which one is more destructive, a drought or a flood? Explain your reasoning. Ki-pat stayed to help the animals and the Kapiti Plain. Would you stay or leave? Explain.

Follow-Up Activities

Bringing the Rain to Kapiti Plain

- Have students create a rhyme or poem about a form of weather (rain, snow, wind, sunshine, etc.). Think about all of their senses and the effects of the weather on the environment and their lives.
- Have students research and recommend ways they can conserve water in their homes and schools. Investigate the history of droughts in the local area and how the community dealt with the severe weather. Present their findings in a variety of ways.
- Simulate a mini-drought experiment using two plants. Water one plant regularly and the other plant very little. Chart what happens to each plant over time to see the effects of the different levels of water on the plants. Analyze and synthesize the data to foster understanding.
- Ask students to invent a tool or object that could help with issues related to weather, similar to Ki-Pat's arrow. These items could be realistic or more imaginative. Use a variety of resources and report on the origins of the resources, as well as the purpose of the invention. Share the inventions in a variety of ways.
- Dramatize the story of *Bringing the Rain to Kapiti Plain*. Pay close attention to the various roles and changes with the different plants and animals. Have students become experts on their roles in order to bring their parts to life.
- Observe the schoolyard and/or location in the community throughout the year. Pay close attention to the effects of the weather on the organisms and the habitat. Collect and share the data in a variety of formats, including digital imagery and science logs.
- Study other legends regarding scientific topics. Compare and contrast legends with factual/scientific reasoning. Consider the cultural significance of legends and create their own legend regarding a science topic of interest. Publish these in a book format.
- Research other specific interests, curiosities, and general information about the basic needs of organisms, African habitats, interdependency of organisms and environment, and severe weather. Provide and encourage the use of multiple sources of information. Have students share their learning in a variety of ways.

Cloudy With a Chance of Meatballs

Written by: Judi Barrett
Published by: Aladdin Paperbacks

Major Topics:

Organisms – Humans, Basic Needs, Behavior
Personal Health – Food, Nutrition
Resources – Natural, Manmade
Weather – Types, Changes

National Science Education Content Standards (1996)

Earth and Space Science

- Changes in the Earth and Sky
- Objects in the Sky

Life Science

- The Characteristics of Organisms
- Organisms and Their Environments

Science in Personal and Social Perspectives

- Personal Health
- Types of Resources
- Changes in the Environment

Summary:

While tucking his grandchildren into bed, Grandpa tells a tall tale about a special town where instead of rain, snow, or sleet falling as precipitation, meatballs, cheese, and pancakes fall from the sky. In this town of Chewandswallow, all weather is in the form of food, and the people use the food in many different ways. However, one day as the portions and sizes of the food get larger and larger, the weather takes a turn for the worse. Tornadoes of pepper and salt blow in and pancakes large enough to cover buildings fall from the sky. Residents of Chewandswallow have to take cover from the weather, eventually abandon the town on boats made from bread, and start a new life where food does not fall from the sky.

Science Concept Map

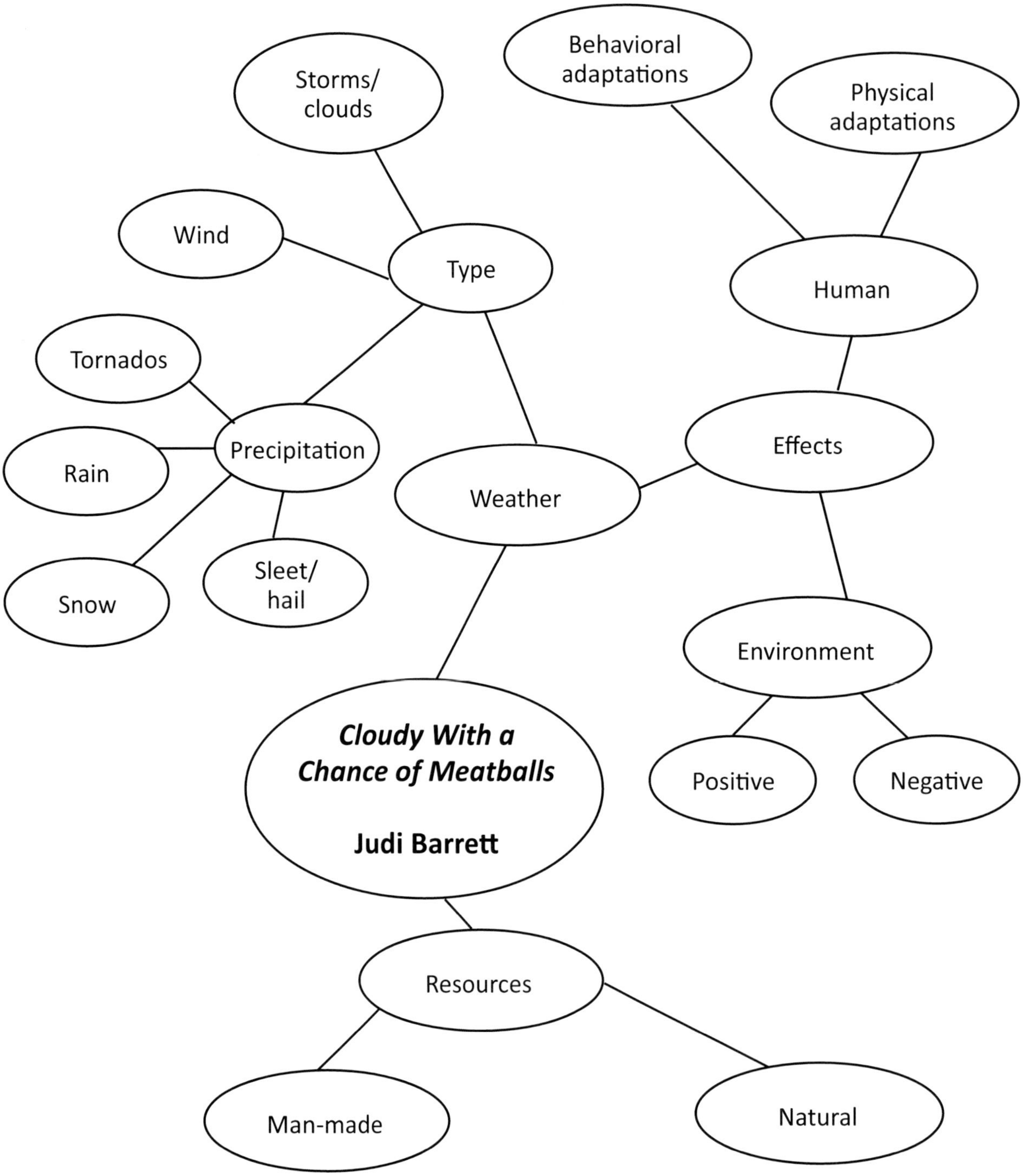

Thinking Questions Based on Bloom's Taxonomy: *Cloudy With a Chance of Meatballs*

1. **Knowledge:**
   Instead of rain or snow, what fell from the sky in Chewandswallow? What types of weather did the people of Chewandswallow experience? Instead of going to the store, how did the people get food? When the people left, what did they use to make their boats?

2. **Comprehension:**
   How did the people use the food that fell from the sky? What were some of the ways the people of Chewandswallow used the extra food? Describe a typical meal in Chewandswallow. Summarize why the people of Chewandswallow left the town.

3. **Application:**
   If you were a resident of Chewandswallow, how would you adapt to the various food storms? How do you adapt to different weather where you live now? Predict what your town would do if it experienced a tornado, hurricane, or flood. If you lived in Chewandswallow describe a balanced meal that you would want to fall from the sky. What type of weather gear would you need if you lived in Chewandswallow?

4. **Analysis:**
   Compare and contrast the weather in Chewandswallow when it was "normal" to the weather when the people left the town. Compare and contrast the weather in Chewandswallow with the weather where you live. What kinds of benefits did the people of Chewandswallow get from the food that fell from the sky? What kinds of problems did it cause? Think about the needs of plants and animals. Do you think the residents of Chewandswallow eat balanced meals? Choose a meal and explain if it is balanced or not. How were the specific nutritional needs of the older generation and younger generation met in this town? People with allergies?

5. **Synthesis:**
   Invent new ways for the people to use the food that fell from the sky in Chewandswallow. If a person wants to make sure that he or she has balanced meals every day, would it be better to live in Chewandswallow or our town? Explain your answer. How did things change for the people when they moved away?

6. **Evaluation:**
   Do you think the people should have left the town? Why? Why not? The citizens of Chewandswallow put extra food in the ocean. If you were a fish, how would you feel about food being put in your environment? Determine which environment you would rather live in — an environment that rained food or water? Explain.

Follow-Up Activities

Cloudy With a Chance of Meatballs

- Study the "water cycle" that exists in Chewandswalllow. Research and investigate Earth's water cycle. Compare and contrast the two cycles. Consider the needs of organisms and weather patterns.

- Invite a meteorologist to speak and answer questions about how he or she predicts and tracks the weather. Learn about tools that support weather prediction and measurement. Develop and broadcast weather for daily school programming.

- Set up an experiment to see what happens to various foods and materials in water. See if they float or sink. Discover which types of food (bread, fruit, vegetables, etc.) would be best to use to get away from Chewandswallow in the water. Create mini-boats/rafts with different types of foods. Consider how much weight the various boats will hold and the properties of the food items.

- Experiment with oil and water. Study the properties of each and how they interact with each other. Consider how oil, human food, and trash affect the ocean environment, sea creatures, and birds.

- Create a Chewandswallow news broadcast. Have students act out feature stories, human-interest stories, a weather report, and so forth. Alternatively, create a news alert bulletin describing the changes in the Chewandswallow weather.

- Explore new uses for ordinary foods. Have students design an invention using what might be left laying around in Chewandswallow. Create a food-invention museum.

- Have students maintain a log of what they eat to see if their diet is balanced. Identify ways that they might adjust their eating habits in order to have a more balanced and nutritious diet.

- Have students develop the ending of the story further. Create multiple endings and consider how the people would adapt to their new habitats. Produce a dramatization or publish a book with the new ending(s).

- Going outside to catch food as it falls from the sky must get tiresome. Have students invent a machine/gadget that can help to collect food. Describe the invention using written and visual formats.

- Research other specific interests, curiosities, and general information about basic needs of organisms, food and nutrition, resources, and weather. Encourage the use of multiple sources of information and sharing in a variety of ways.

Come On, Rain!

Written by: Karen Hesse
Published by: Scholastic, Inc.

Major Topics:

Organisms – Animals/Humans, Plants, Basic Needs, Behaviors
Weather – Environment Changes, Rain, Drought, Water Cycle

National Science Education Content Standards (1996)

Life Science

- The Characteristics of Organisms
- Organisms and Their Environments

Earth and Space Science

- Changes in the Earth and Sky

Science in Personal and Social Perspectives

- Changes in the Environment

Summary:

In the midst of a summer drought, Tess, a young girl living in an urban area, sees her mother's frustration as they experience the heat and lack of rain. Tess observes how the tar is hot, the plants are drooping, and the children are kept inside the house to keep cool and not burn in the hot sun. When Tess notices gray clouds in the distance, she pleads to the sky, "Come on, Rain!" Tess and her friends are excited in anticipation of the rain. When it finally rains, her friends and their mothers rejoice and dance in the rain, as everything begins to spring back to life.

Science Concept Map

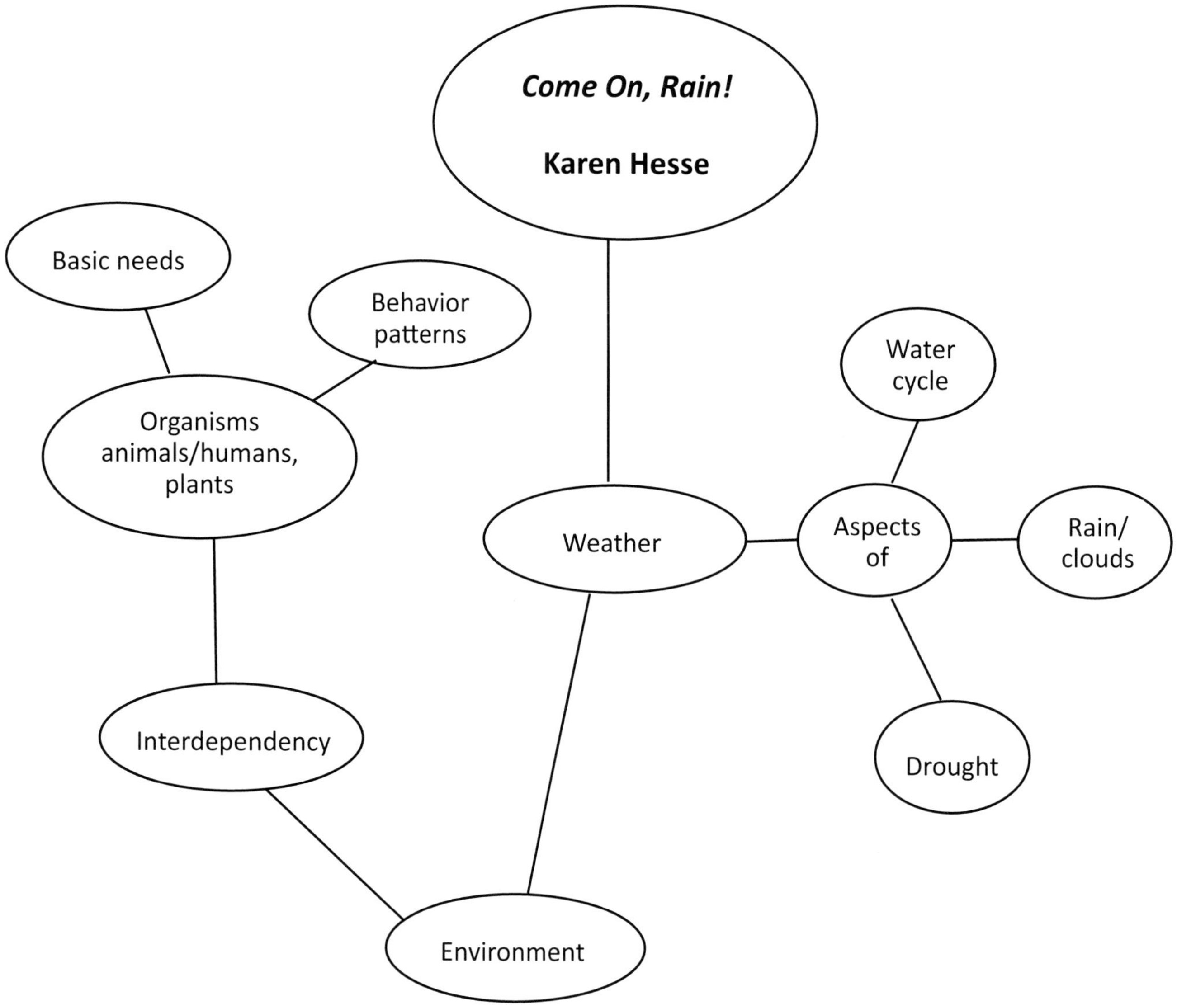

Thinking Questions Based on Bloom's Taxonomy: *Come On, Rain!*

1. **Knowledge:**
   What was the main problem in the story? What was affected by the drought or lack of rain? When the rain came, what changed?

2. **Comprehension:**
   Retell the events of the story. Why did Tess, her mother, and the other characters want it to rain? Describe the things Tess and her mother did to adapt to the drought. How did Tess know that the rain was coming? Why did Tess want to put on her bathing suit? How did the rain affect the environment?

3. **Application:**
   If it had not rained, what would have happened to Tess's mother's plants? The people? The environment? How would you solve the problem of not having enough rain? Think about your own home/neighborhood and predict what would happen to the plants if there was too much or too little rain. What else could have been done to support the plants growing? How do you adapt to weather and climate change in your city/town?

4. **Analysis:**
   Describe the relationship between the clouds and the rain. Categorize the effects of the drought and rain on the community into social behaviors and environmental/physical effects. Compare and contrast the environment before and after it rained. Consider the effects on plants, animals, the physical environment, and people. When the rain finally came, how did the characters react?

5. **Synthesis:**
   Explain why the rain was important to the community, plants, and animals in the story. Discuss why you think that Tess's mother was so sad and frustrated during the drought and so happy when the rain finally came. Does everything on Earth, including humans, need rain to survive? What are other basic needs for living things on Earth?

6. **Evaluation:**
   Do you think it's important to save water during a drought? Why or why not? Tess's mother did not hand-water her plants during the drought. Was this a good idea to wait for rain instead? Explain your thinking. Did the community deal with the lack of rain well? Explain.

Follow-Up Activities

Come On, Rain!

- Experiment with ways to better foster plant growth during a simulated drought. Help students generalize their thoughts in order to demonstrate their understanding of the basic needs for plant growth.

- Have students research and discover plants that live in conditions that are different from those of their own environment. Request that students concentrate on plants that may live in extreme conditions. For example, have students study plants that would thrive in areas of drought like the desert or under the conditions where Tess lived.

- As a class, develop a sensory poem describing how people, animals, and the environment react and feel when there is not enough rain (drought) and when rain comes.

- Recreate the story and change the setting to match the students' environment. Consider the plants and animals in their local area as well as their own reactions. Have students use descriptive language in their writing and create visual images to add to the story as well. Publish their version of *Come On, Rain!* in electronic or written format.

- Investigate water conservation efforts in the students' communities and/or cities. Have students develop a water conservation plan for their classroom, school, or homes.

- Study the water cycle, its importance to the Earth, and its weather patterns. Analyze how intense weather events, such as a flood, blizzard, or wind storm affect the environment.

- Read literature from other cultures or time periods about the importance of rain. Based on the stories, what roles did/does rain play in other cultures? Develop their own stories.

- Research other specific interests, curiosities, and general information about the basic needs of organisms, environment changes, weather, and the water cycle. Provide and encourage the use of multiple sources of information. Have students share their learning in a variety of ways.

The Empty Lot

Written by: Dale H. Fife
Published by: Sierra Club Books for Children

Major Topics:

Environment – Changes, Issues, Interdependency
Organisms – Animals, Plants, Basic Needs, Behaviors, Habitat

National Science Education Content Standards (1996)

Life Science

- The Characteristics of Organisms
- Organisms and Their Environments

Science in Personal and Social Perspectives

- Changes in the Environment

Summary:

Before Harry Hale sells the empty lot he owns to developers, he visits it one last time. On his visit to the lot, he is shocked to find that it is not in the middle of a small town anymore, but surrounded by factories, shops, and schools. As he walks through the lot, Harry realizes the lot is not empty at all, but in fact, occupied. His lot is a habitat for birds, insects, trees, and many other living things. As a result, Harry decides not to sell the lot to the developers, but instead to maintain the natural habitat.

Science Concept Map

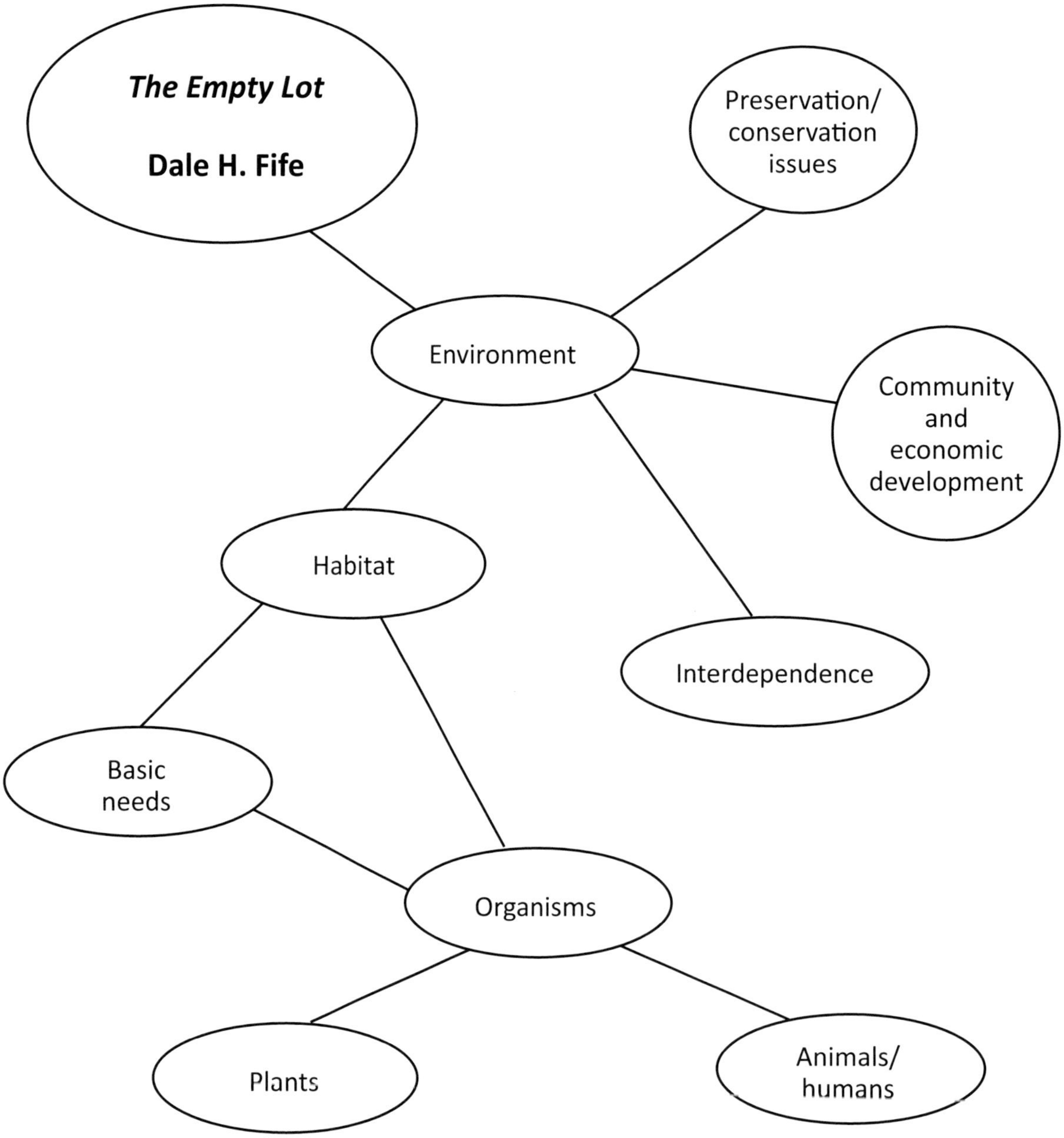

Thinking Questions Based on Bloom's Taxonomy: *The Empty Lot*

1. **Knowledge:**
   What did Harry want to do with the lot before he visited it? After he visited it? What were some of the things Harry observed while visiting the lot? Where was the lot located? Was the area around the lot the same as Harry remembered?

2. **Comprehension:**
   Discuss some of the ways the lot served as a habitat for living things. Describe Harry's feelings about the lot when he visited it. Why did Harry want to sell the lot at first? Why did Harry change his mind about selling the lot?

3. **Application:**
   Pretend you are interviewing one of the animals that lived in the lot. What would it say if you asked why it chose the lot as its home? Think of at least one area in or around the school that is a habitat for plants or animals. What things live there now? What things may have lived there before the school was built? Predict what the school lot will be like in 5 years.

4. **Analysis:**
   Describe the process Harry went through to decide what to do with the lot. Identify the possible reasons why the area around the lot was developed with factories and other buildings. Compare and contrast these changes with changes in your own community. Compare and contrast man-made habitats and natural habitats (e.g., zoo vs. forest). How is a man-made habitat similar to or different from a natural habitat?

5. **Synthesis:**
   At the end of the story, what were Harry's views about "empty lots"? What did he mean by writing on the sign, "Every square inch in use"? If Harry had decided to sell the lot, hypothesize what would have happened to the living things that lived in the lot. Propose a plan of action for there to be a balance between developed and natural areas in Harry's community. How could the factories, schools, or churches support a natural habitat in the community?

6. **Evaluation:**
   Imagine you are Harry. What would you do with the lot? Why? If you went to buy the lot from Harry, what would you do? Why? Do you think that Harry made a good decision not to sell his lot? Should he have sold the lot anyway? Why or why not?

Follow-Up Activities

The Empty Lot

- Go on a walk and observe animal and plant habitats around the schoolyard. Study the habitats closely. How do the organisms thrive in them? Discuss the similarities and differences of these habitats. Develop a "habitat map" of the schoolyard with accompanying guides.

- Investigate, discuss, and determine what area of the school yard needs support to become or be a better natural habitat for plants and animals. Plan, develop, and implement a way to do this. Involve other school staff in the plan.

- Explore "empty lots" outside the classroom and decide if they are empty or occupied. Give each student a designated area and a recording sheet for their observations. Use a magnifying lens, digital camera, and their own eyes to make observations about their lots. Determine what exists in their space and present data to support their conclusion on whether the lot is empty or occupied. As a whole class, gather, analyze, and synthesize the data that was collected.

- Contact a local agency involved with planning, development, and/or conservation in their town. Gather information and future plans for the community and local area. After this research, have students make recommendations on future community development projects that will both benefit the community economically and preserve natural habitats.

- Research different perspectives of the environmental issues presented in the book. Debate different viewpoints. For example, consider building societal wants/needs versus maintenance of natural habitats.

- The story ends when Harry changes the sign to an "occupied lot." Continue the story from where it ended. Develop multiple possible endings that would be considered "happy" or "sad" based on the perspective. Write these endings in a book or act them out.

- Have students pretend they wanted to sell the lot. Design a visual to convince buyers that the lot is "empty." Design another visual to convince the community that the lot is "occupied."

- Research other specific interests, curiosities, and general information about the basic needs of organisms, changes in the environment, current environment issues, and interdependence. Provide and encourage the use of multiple sources of information. Have students share their learning in a variety of ways.

The First Strawberries

Written by: Joseph Bruchac
Published by: Dial Books for Young Readers

Major Topics:

Organisms – Plants, Basic Needs, Characteristics, Habitat

National Science Education Content Standards (1996)

Life Science

- The Characteristics of Organisms
- Life Cycle of Organisms
- Organisms and Their Environment

Summary:

This Cherokee legend explains the origin of the strawberry. A long time ago, when the world had just begun, there was a couple who was happily married, until one day they got in an argument and the woman walked away from her husband. Desperate to get his wife back but too slow to catch her, the man sought help from the Sun. The Sun sent berries to grow in the woman's path in an attempt to stop her. Raspberries, blueberries, nor blackberries slowed her down, until the Sun put strawberry plants in her path. The beauty of the strawberries made the woman stop to pick and eat them, and as a result her husband was able to catch up with her and reconcile their relationship. According to Cherokee legend, this was the first appearance of the strawberry.

Science Concept Map

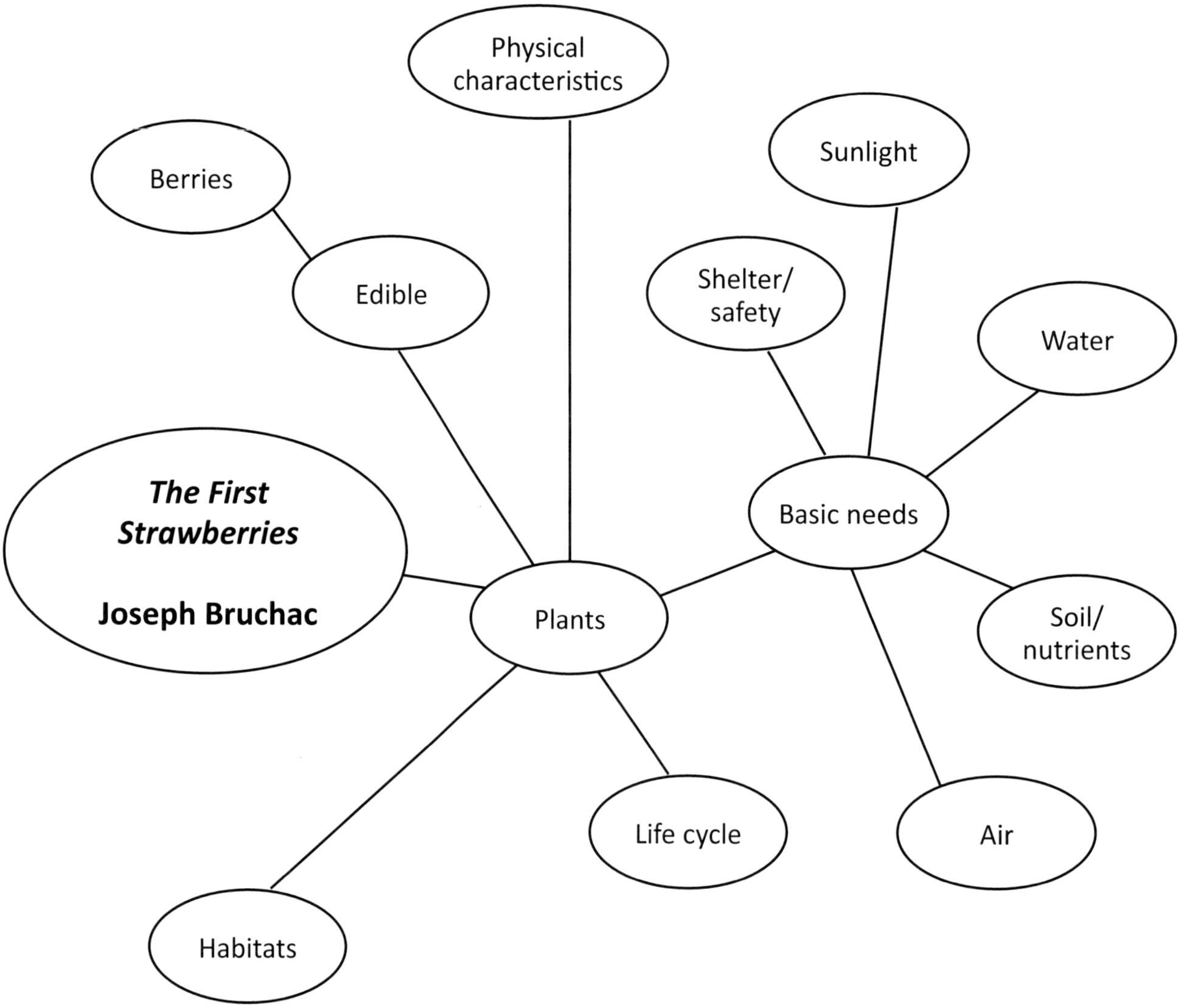

Thinking Questions Based on Bloom's Taxonomy: *The First Strawberries*

1. **Knowledge:**
   List the different types of plants the Sun made grow in the woman's path. In what type of environment/habitat did this couple live? What eventually made the woman stop walking?

2. **Comprehension:**
   Retell the events of the story. Explain how the berries grew. How did the Sun help the man? Why did she stop walking for the strawberries?

3. **Application:**
   Predict what would happen to the berries without the Sun. How would you create a perfect environment for a plant to grow? Think about scientific and cultural aspects. Give examples of other edible plants and fruits that you may see in a meadow.

4. **Analysis:**
   Categorize different types of fruits and plants in the story. Determine factors that helped the berries grow. Identify the needs of a plant. How did the Sun create the perfect environment to grow the strawberries? Be specific.

5. **Synthesis:**
   The Sun made the berries appear in the legend. What is the role of the sun scientifically in the life cycle of a plant? Describe what you would need to have a berry garden at school. Consider the needs of plants, supplies for your garden, and how you plan to take care of it.

6. **Evaluation:**
   The woman stopped to smell and investigate the strawberries. Was this a good choice, in your opinion? Why or why not? Would you have been most interested in the strawberries, or would another kind of fruit have been more interesting to you? Explain your answer with reasons. The Sun chose to help the man with his situation. Was this a good choice? Why or why not?

Follow-Up Activities

The First Strawberries

- Plan, plant, and nurture a class garden. Collect data on plant growth. Compare and contrast the life cycles of the various plants included in your garden. Consider planting various berries. Study the life cycle of berries and their plants. Determine the function of a berry.

- Make observations of a variety of fruits. Work with students to develop a list of questions on which to base their observations. Go on field studies in and outside of school where they can interact with a variety of fruits, and possibly harvest some. Talk to a farmer or grocer about the growing processes of fruits and their life cycle. Develop a "fruit findings" book or visual including all of the findings.

- Compare and contrast different types of fruits and plants. Research and investigate fruits and vegetables. What are differences? Similarities? Use realia as well as other information in their investigation.

- Survey students, family, and friends. Collect data to answer the question: What kinds of fruit do students in our class like? Why? Analyze and synthesize the data in a variety of ways.

- Play "Guess My Fruit." Make up clues to describe a mystery fruit. Have students share their clues and let the other students guess. Use this opportunity to talk about attributes and physical characteristics of these objects.

- Study the scientific history of the strawberry. Refer to web sites and other material to gain a better understanding.

- Research other specific interests, curiosities, and general information about basic needs, habitats, and plants. Provide and encourage the use of multiple sources of information. Have students share their learning in a variety of ways.

Fish is Fish

Written and Illustrated by: Leo Lionni
Published by: Dragonfly Books

Major Topics:

Organisms – Fish, Frogs, Basic Needs, Behaviors, Habitat, Life Cycle, Physical Characteristics

National Science Education Content Standards (1996)

Life Science

- The Characteristics of Organisms
- Life Cycles of Organisms
- Organisms and Their Environments

Summary:

A minnow and a tadpole live together in a pond and are the best of friends. As they become adults, the tadpole becomes a frog, and the minnow becomes a fish. The adult frog must now go on land to live and explore the world, leaving the fish in the pond. One day when the frog comes back, it tells the fish of all of the wonderful things it has seen, such as birds, cows, and people. The fish decides it wants to see the world too and jumps out of the water onto the riverbank, only to find that it cannot breathe on the land habitat. The frog comes to his rescue by pushing the fish back in the pond habitat. The fish reenergizes in his pond habitat and realizes that it does not belong on land, but in its own "most beautiful world of all worlds" — because a fish is a fish.

Science Concept Map

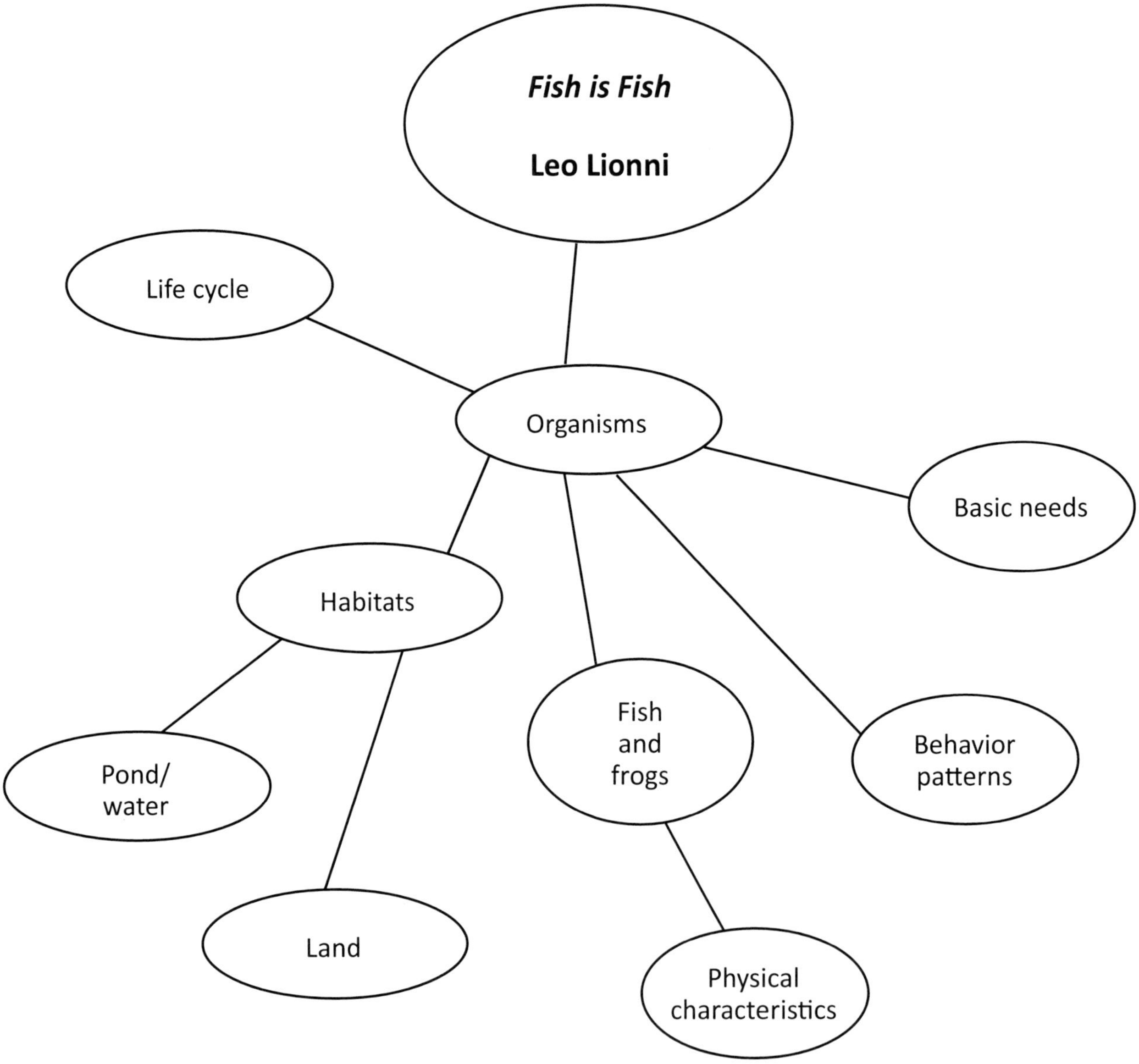

Fish is Fish

Leo Lionni

- Organisms
  - Life cycle
  - Basic needs
  - Habitats
    - Pond/ water
    - Land
  - Fish and frogs
    - Physical characteristics
  - Behavior patterns

Thinking Questions Based on Bloom's Taxonomy: *Fish is Fish*

1. **Knowledge:**
Name the two animals in the beginning of the story. What types of animals do they become as adults? What things did the frog see in the world outside of the water? Where did the minnow and tadpole live? When they become adults, where did the frog and fish live? Where did the fish want to go?

2. **Comprehension:**
How did the frog's body change as it became an adult? Did these changes prepare its body for land? Why was the water the best habitat for the fish? Why did the frog leave the pond? Why did the fish want to leave the pond at first? How did the fish envision the animals on land? What would have happened to the fish if the frog was not nearby to help?

3. **Application:**
Imagine a human living in the water, and explain what types of adaptations he or she would have to make. What type of physical characteristics would be necessary? Look at animals in your life, at school, home, or outside. How do they survive in their environments? Think about astronauts; how do they adapt their bodies to visit outer space? How could humans live in outer space forever?

4. **Analysis:**
Compare and contrast the fish and the frog. Analyze the life cycles, the habitats, and their physical characteristics. Compare and contrast the two habitats, pond and land. How are the fish and frog specifically adapted to live in their environments? Think about a human's needs. What would be the best habitat for a human?

5. **Synthesis:**
Imagine that fish could live outside of the water. What kinds of bodies would they have to have in order to make this possible? How are all animals connected to their habitats? Why did the fish imagine the land animals as it did? Defend the fish's reasons for wanting to stay in the water by the end of the story. How was the frog able to survive at one point in the water habitat and then on land? Could the frog have lived completely in the water as an adult? Explain its life cycle.

6. **Evaluation:**
Which animal from the story — fish or frog — would you rather be? Explain your choice. Would you want to live like another animal? Explain your ideas.

Follow-Up Activities

Fish is Fish

- Raise animals in the classroom that have a relatively short and unique life cycle. Consider mealworms, tadpoles, or caterpillars. Have students keep an observation log as they watch the animal's life cycle and then research background information.

- Take a trip to a pond and observe animals and plants in their natural habitat. Have students generalize characteristics of plants and animals that thrive in a pond environment. Gather data using a variety of means and share conclusions in both visual and written formats.

- Have students use various art materials to create an imaginary animal with certain physical characteristics for surviving in its unique habitat. Have students explain why they created the animal and how its new adaptations allow it to survive. For example, create a picture or model of a fish that has physical traits that will allow it to survive on land. Explain the modifications to the features of the fish that allows it to survive on land.

- Study the physical characteristics of one or more animals. Identify how that animal's features help it survive in its natural environment. Consider all of the animal's basic needs when analyzing.

- Have students act out the life cycle of a fish and a frog. Create visual and written explanations of these changes as well. Compare and contrast the life cycles with other animals' life cycles. Consider studying reptiles, amphibians, birds, fish, and mammals.

- Have students find and cut out pictures in magazines and catalogs showing humans at different stages of life. Group pictures by the different stages. Write about the life cycle of humans and how humans relate to their environment.

- Research other specific interests, curiosities, and basic information about organisms (fish, frog) and related habitats. Provide and encourage the use of multiple sources of information. Have students share their learning in a variety of ways.

Germs

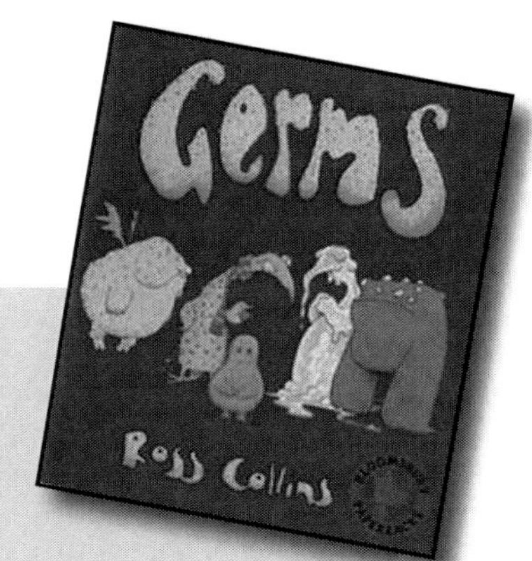

Written and Illustrated by: Ross Collins
Published by: Bloomsbury Children's Books

Major Topics:

Organisms – Humans, Environment, Immune System
Personal Health – Communicable Diseases, Germs

National Science Education Content Standards (1996)

Life Science

- The Characteristics of Organisms
- Organisms and Their Environments

Science in Personal and Social Perspectives

- Personal Health

Summary:

Even after attending Germ Academy to learn how to be an infectious germ and proving that he is unhealthy, a germ named Pox does not understand why he should want to infect a child and get him or her sick. When Pox is sent on his first mission to infect a young girl named Myrtle, he refuses to carry out his duties and decides to join forces with the immune system instead. As other germs from the Academy arrive, Pox uses all he learned at Germ Academy to prevent Myrtle from becoming sick. To honor him, the immune system invites him to stay in Myrtle's body and become their leader in the fight to keep her healthy.

Science Concept Map

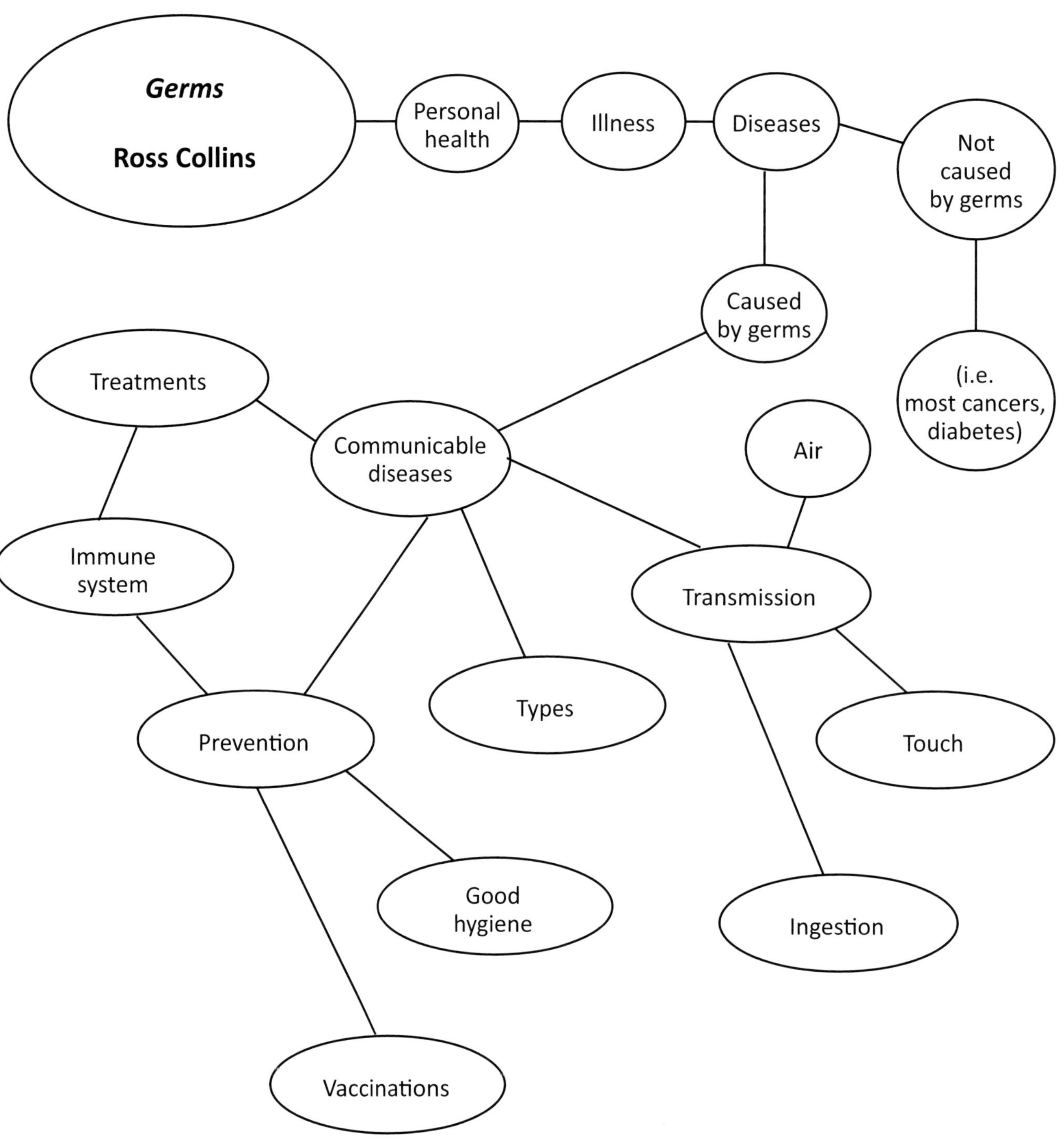

Thinking Questions Based on Bloom's Taxonomy: *Germs*

1. **Knowledge:**
   What is Pox? What does Pox learn at Germ Academy? Who are his germ roommates? When he enters Myrtle, who does he encounter? Does he fight the immune system? Does Myrtle end up getting sick? Who gets sick instead?

2. **Comprehension:**
   According to the story, what is the purpose of most germs? How was Pox supposed to infect Myrtle? Does Pox like being a germ that gets people sick? How does he help to prevent Myrtle from getting sick? How did the dog end up being infected? Why was Pox considered a hero by Myrtle's immune system?

3. **Application:**
   How do you stay healthy? We sneeze, cough, and blow our noses a lot at school. How can we keep ourselves protected from the spread of germs? What are good hygiene practices? How do you support your immune system? What really happens when a germ enters the human body?

4. **Analysis:**
   Think about what Germ Academy was like. What are the main ways germs infect humans? (Think about the "Points of Attack.") Explain how germs are transmitted from one individual to another. What is the main purpose of the immune system?

5. **Synthesis:**
   Predict what would happen to you if you did not prevent the spread of germs. Determine ways to prevent the spread of illnesses. How does a human body stay healthy and react to germs? Are all germs harmful to the body? Discuss how some germs help our bodies.

6. **Evaluation:**
   Would you rather be a germ or a member of the immune system? Explain your thinking. Pox took a risk and went against his community and what he was supposed to do. Do you agree with his decision? Was that a hard decision to make? Explain your thinking.

Follow-Up Activities

Germs

- Compare how the germs act in the story to how they behave scientifically in real life. Research and investigate communicable diseases. Research the basic facts, history, source, and treatments for each. Compare and contrast the different diseases.

- Discuss good hygiene practices, such as washing your hands, brushing your teeth, or covering your mouth when you sneeze. Write a guide and then demonstrate and practice good hygiene practices. Become a "Germ Patrol" at school and share what you learned with other classes. Create posters to remind students at home and at school how to stay healthy.

- Create a skit in which students perform the different characters in the book *Germs.* Share with other classes and follow up with discussions regarding health issues.

- Demonstrate the spreading of germs. Have students put lotion on their hands and sprinkle a little bit of glitter on each student's hands. Tell the students that the glitter lotion represents germs. Throughout the day, notice the glitter on objects throughout the classroom. This shows how easily germs spread. Follow up with a lesson on hand washing and preventative measures.

- Determine foods that build and support the immune system. Advocate for more of these foods at home and at school. Write letters or make presentations to share their viewpoint.

- Study the role of vaccinations and medicine in relation to disease control. Research historical illnesses and how we have combated them as a community (e.g., polio, plague).

- Contact a local health agency and/or invite an epidemiologist to come and share about the study of disease — where we are and how far we have come. Look at current trends and issues.

- Research other specific interests, curiosities, and basic information about communicable diseases, germs, immune system, and personal health. Provide and encourage the use of multiple sources of information. Have students share their learning in a variety of ways.

The Great Kapok Tree: A Tale of the Amazon Rain Forest

Written and Illustrated by: Lynne Cherry
Published by: Voyager Books/Harcourt

Major Topics:

Environment – Rain forest, Issues, Preservation
Organisms – Animals/Humans, Plants, Basic Needs, Habitat, Interdependency

National Science Education Content Standards (1996)

Life Science

- The Characteristics of Organisms
- Organisms and Their Environments

Science in Personal and Social Perspectives

- Changes in the Environment

Summary:

A young man enters the Amazon rain forest with the intention of chopping down a great Kapok tree. But when he falls asleep under the tree, the animals who live in the rain forest explain to him how important the Kapok tree is to their survival. The young man learns about the interdependency that exists among the animals, plants, and people who live in the rain forest. When he awakens he is able to see the rain forest with "new eyes" and decides to leave and not cut down the great Kapok tree.

Science Concept Map

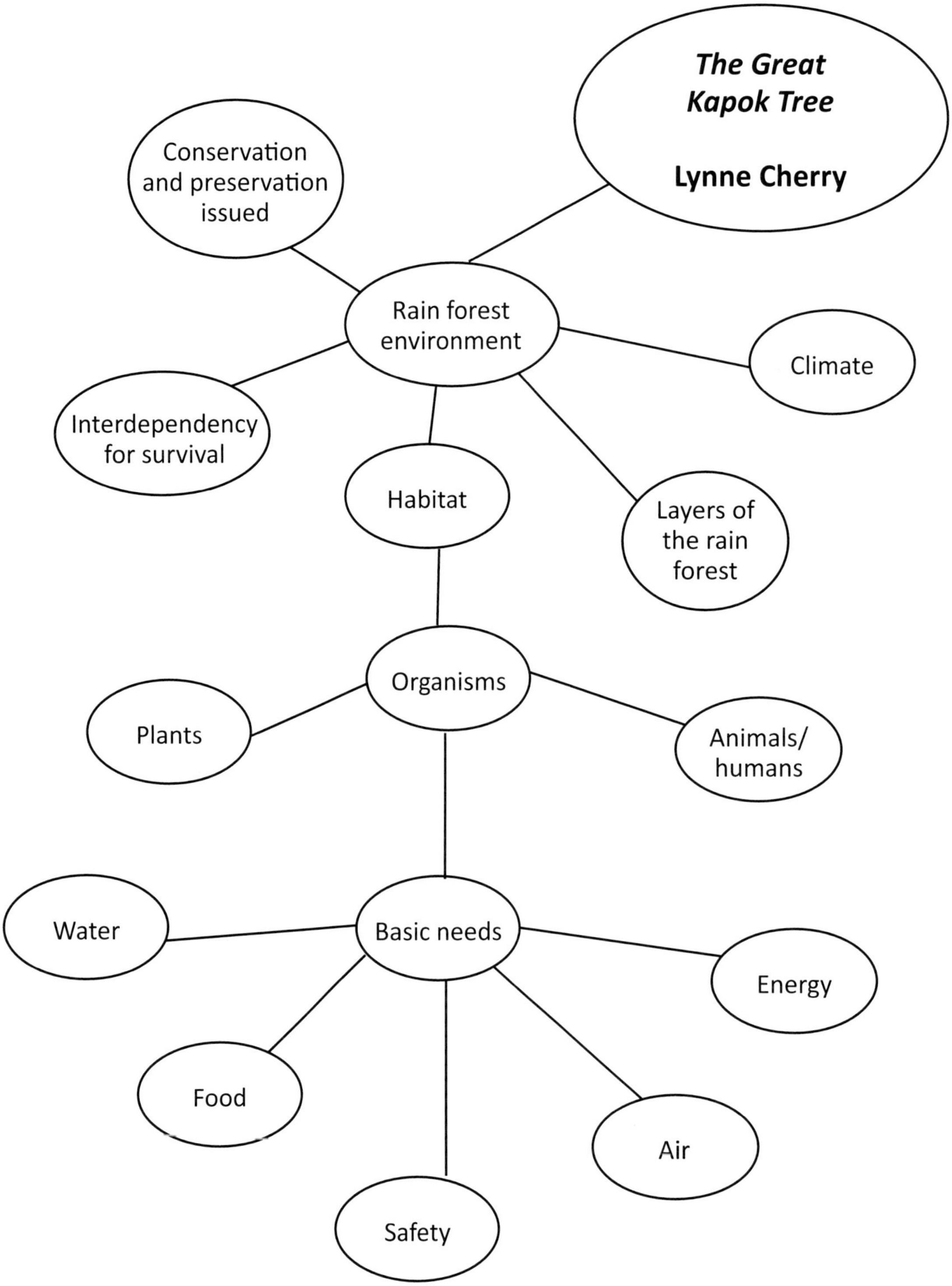

The Great Kapok Tree

Lynne Cherry

Conservation and preservation issued

Rain forest environment

Climate

Interdependency for survival

Habitat

Layers of the rain forest

Organisms

Plants

Animals/ humans

Water

Basic needs

Energy

Food

Air

Safety

Thinking Questions Based on Bloom's Taxonomy: *The Great Kapok Tree*

1. **Knowledge:**
   What was the man supposed to do in the rain forest? What happened when the man fell asleep? What happened when he woke up? Name some of the animals in the story. Did the animal and human inhabitants want the Kapok tree cut down?

2. **Comprehension:**
   Describe the rain forest environment, including the weather. Why did the man fall asleep under the tree? Why did the man change his mind and not cut down the Kapok tree? How did the rain forest inhabitants convince the man not to cut down the tree? Explain some of the reasons given.

3. **Application:**
   How have places in your school yard and community affected the natural habitat of organisms? How have humans impacted the environment? What roles do plants play in your environment? What role can you play in preserving the rain forest?

4. **Analysis:**
   Imagine if the man had cut down the Kapok tree. What would have happened to the plants, the trees, the rain forest, and the people? Predict what the smaller man would have said to the larger man when he returned without having cut down the Kapok tree. What did all of the animals' messages have in common? How did they differ?

5. **Synthesis:**
   Explain why the animals need the Kapok tree. Based on the story, determine the key reasons not to destroy the Kapok tree. How would cutting down the trees in the Amazon rain forest affect the people and animals living in the rain forest? How are humans, animals, and plants interdependent?

6. **Evaluation:**
   Which reason shared by the rain forest inhabitants was the most convincing to you? Which would have changed your mind? Would you have cut down the tree or walked away? Explain.

Follow-Up Activities

The Great Kapok Tree

- Continue the story from where it ended. What happens next after the man leaves? Make a big book with a follow-up story.
- Investigate the physical properties of the layers of the rain forest. Study the animals, plants, and other aspects of each layer. Create visual and written projects.
- Research why rain forests are cut down. What are the benefits? What are the costs? Explain each position. Have a mock debate on the issue.
- Design a food chain that shows how the organisms in the rain forest are dependent on each other for survival. Study specific animal characteristics and needs. Make a creative product showing this food chain, like a mobile or puzzle.
- As a class or individually, contact a rain forest conservation/preservation organization. Gather a variety of information. Develop a proposal to save the Amazon rain forest. Consider current plans and issues facing the communities.
- Research rain forests from around the world. Chart locations and size. Compare and contrast the characteristics, inhabitants, and the current trends and issues of destruction/preservation of the rain forests. Synthesize the information gathered and create a "Rain Forests Around the World" book.
- Discuss and explore the consequences of destruction of the rain forest in small increments over long periods of time as compared with rain forest destruction in large increments over short periods of time. Consult different resources and perspectives to understand the issues completely. Present information as a debate or point/counterpoint article in the school paper.
- Research and find communities in your state that have been affected by the cutting down of trees. Study the background, implications, and consequences of this situation.
- Research other specific interests, curiosities, and basic information about the rain forest environment and organisms. Provide and encourage the use of multiple sources of information. Have students share their learning in a variety of ways.

Gregory, the Terrible Eater

Written by: Mitchell Sharmat
Published by: Scholastic Books

Major Topics:

Organisms – Animals, Basic Needs
Personal Health – Nutrition

National Science Education Content Standards (1996)

Life Science

- The Characteristics of Organisms

Science in Personal and Social Perspectives

- Personal Health

Summary:

Gregory is like other goats in many ways except for his eating habits. Unlike other goats in the story, Gregory prefers to eat fruits, vegetables, fish, and bread, much to the chagrin of his parents. As a way of balancing Gregory's diet, his parents ease him into eating portions of "junk" along with his strange taste for healthier food. Their plan succeeds and, at one point, Gregory is eating every "junk" food available to him. Soon, Gregory finds that too much junk in his diet makes him feel bad and settles for a balanced diet of healthy and "junk" food instead.

Science Concept Map

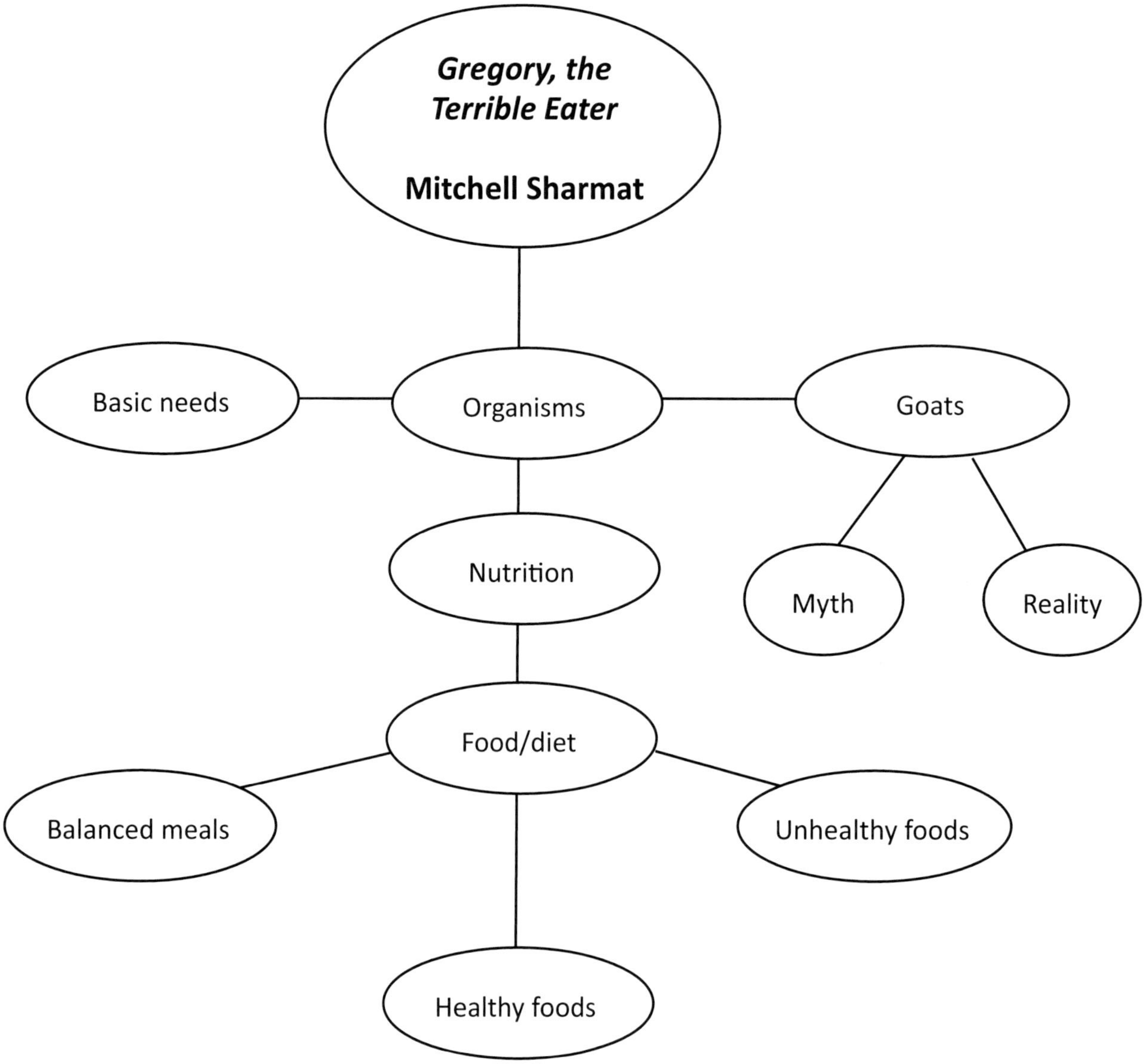

Gregory, the Terrible Eater

Mitchell Sharmat

- Organisms
  - Basic needs
  - Goats
    - Myth
    - Reality
  - Nutrition
    - Food/diet
      - Balanced meals
      - Unhealthy foods
      - Healthy foods

Thinking Questions Based on Bloom's Taxonomy: *Gregory, the Terrible Eater*

1. **Knowledge:**
   Gregory is what type of animal? According to the story, what types of food did Gregory's parents want him to eat? What foods did Gregory want to eat at the beginning of the story? What made Gregory's stomach hurt? At the end, what did Gregory and his parents eat?

2. **Comprehension:**
   Why did all of the goats want him to eat "junk"? Discuss in what ways Gregory's parents tried to get him to eat "junk." Why did too much "junk" food make Gregory sick? Why did Gregory eat a more balanced meal at the end?

3. **Application:**
   Predict what would happen if you ate only junk food and never had any fruits and vegetables. How could eating too much of anything be unhealthy? How can you eat a balanced meal? Share an example.

4. **Analysis:**
   Compare and contrast the types of food that Gregory's parents ate with the types of food that Gregory liked to eat at the beginning. Discuss what is different about these types of food.

5. **Synthesis:**
   When was Gregory a "terrible eater" in the story? At the end of the story, how was he a good eater? How did the meal at the end of the story support healthy nutrition? Why are balanced meals important for all animals, including humans?

6. **Evaluation:**
   Do you think it's a good idea to eat only one type of food? Why or why not? Gregory's parents made him try new foods. Was this a good idea? Explain your thinking.

Follow-Up Activities

Gregory, the Terrible Eater

- Collect food pictures from magazines and have children bring food labels from home or gather some at school. Categorize the different foods based on USDA guidelines and their own thinking. Discuss why different foods belong to certain groups. Use collected food labels and pictures to create combinations of balanced meals. Let students use the food pyramid as a guide to label and discuss the food combinations they develop.

- Research the real eating habits of goats. Compare and contrast this with the eating habits of Gregory and his parents. Have students write an explanation of why they think goats have a reputation of eating trash.

- Have students develop and publish a class cookbook. Create balanced meals to contribute to the cookbook. Cookbooks should include cooking directions, illustrations, ingredients, and meal descriptions.

- As a class, interview food service employees to find out how they decide what combinations of food to serve at school. Collect data on which foods are sold and eaten the most at school. Analyze the data to determine if students eat well.

- Investigate where different foods come from. Create a diagram to show the stages different foods go through before they make it to our plates. What is the role of agriculture and farming in our society? Share findings with the school community.

- Research other specific interests, curiosities, and basic information about organisms, goats, and personal health. Provide and encourage the use of multiple sources of information. Have students share their learning in a variety of ways.

I Took a Walk

Written and Illustrated by: Henry Cole
Published by: Greenwillow Books

Major Topics:

Organisms – Animals, Plants, Basic Needs, Behavior, Habitats

National Science Education Content Standards (1996)

Life Science

- Organisms and Their Environments
- The Characteristics of Organism

Summary:

This story is about a little boy who goes for a walk through the woods and a meadow by a stream and a pond on a spring day. He observes the environment around him and sees many different types of animals and plants. The book shows some of the things you can see in different habitats if you look closely. Some of the things he sees on his walk are a woodpecker in the woods, grasshopper in the meadow, deer tracks on the bank of the river, and a minnow in a pond. Each habitat is illustrated on pull-out pages.

Science Concept Map

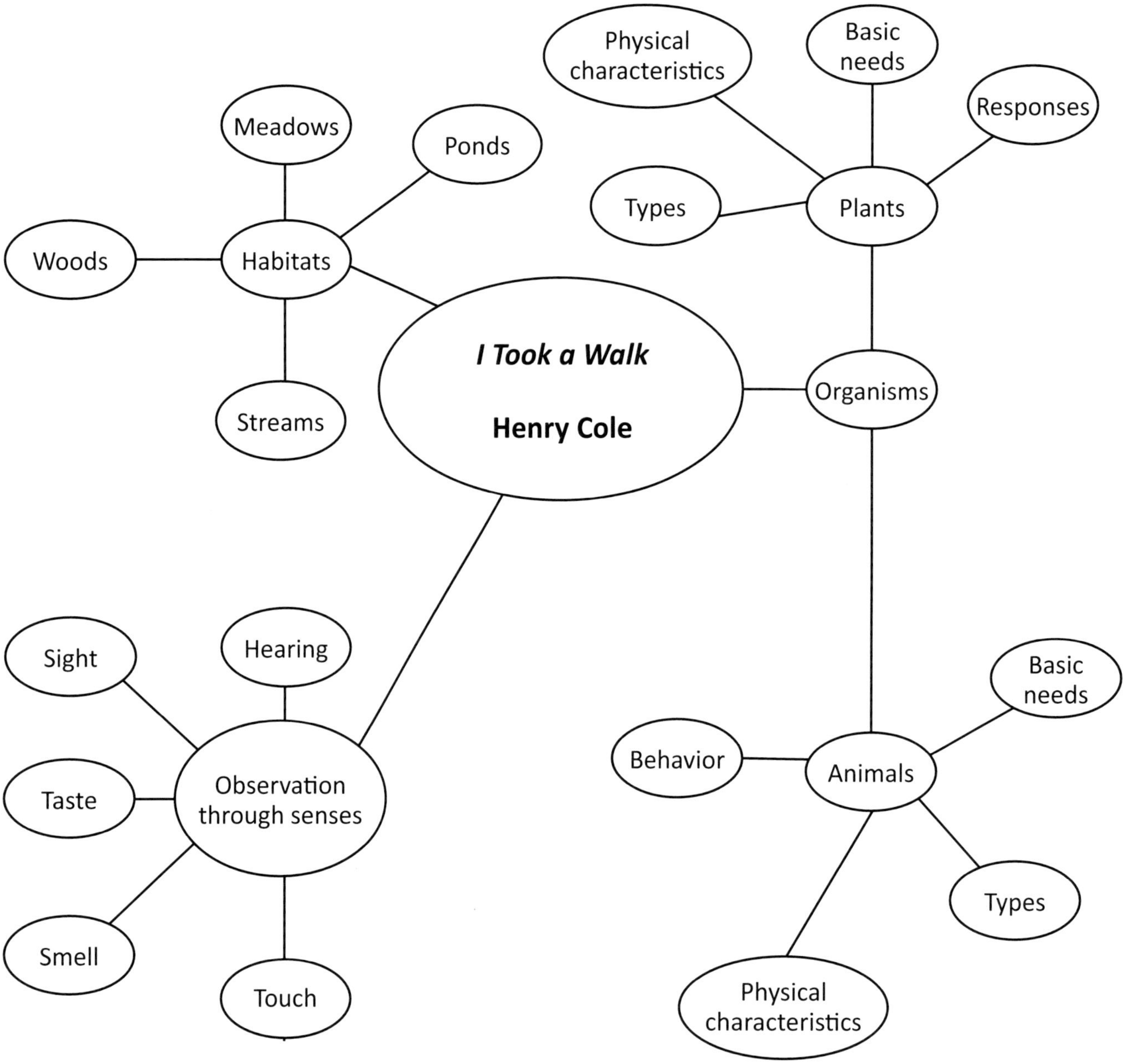

Thinking Questions Based on Bloom's Taxonomy: *I Took a Walk*

1. **Knowledge:**
   Which habitats does the boy visit? What does the boy see in the habitats? Name some of the animals in each habitat. List some types of plants in each habitat. Locate on a specific page what animals/plants you see.

2. **Comprehension:**
   Describe each of the habitats in your own words. How did the boy observe and describe what he noticed in all of the environments? Why did the animals live in a specific habitat?

3. **Application:**
   Predict what would happen if the stream dried out. Imagine if a duck lived in the stream without a lot of water. What would happen? What are some other animals that could thrive in one of the habitats in the story? If you were to walk around your school grounds and look closely, what do you think you might see, hear, smell, and touch?

4. **Analysis:**
   Classify the different types of animals in the habitats. Look at the illustrations. How are some of the physical characteristics of the animals alike or different? Explain why particular animals live in each habitat. Compare and contrast each habitat. In the story, the boy observes "signs of a squirrel" and "signs of a beaver." What are some possible signs the boy might have observed?

5. **Synthesis:**
   Choose an animal from each habitat and tell how it is able to live in that environment. Why is it important for each animal to live in a habitat that meets its needs? Decide which type of plant or animal would live best in your classroom environment. Consider the organism's characteristics in relation to the environment.

6. **Evaluation:**
   Select your favorite habitat from the book. Explain why it is your favorite. What type of habitat from the book would you like to live near? Why?

Follow-Up Activities

I Took a Walk

- Visit various habitats around school and home. Observe the surroundings using particular senses. Make observations using their senses and record in an observation journal. Compare and contrast the boy's observations in the book with their observations. Create a replica of the habitats they observed. Develop a class big book about their observations titled, "I Took a Walk Around the School."

- Research the plants and animals that live in a particular habitat. Create a visual depiction in the form of a museum display, in which the plants and animals are numbered and labeled (similar to the pictures at the end of the book). In written form explain how the habitat is suited to the needs of the organisms that live there.

- Conduct research to learn more about the plants and animals included in this book. Design a game that will help people learn about plants and animals that "belong" in different kinds of habitats. Be sure to include information that explains how the plants and animals are suited to the habitats in which they live.

- Invite a wildlife or environmental specialist to come and share his or her expertise. Have the guest share about how he or she collects information to learn about plants and animals and the wildlife areas with which the specialist comes in contact.

- Research other specific interests, curiosities, and basic information about habitats and organisms. Provide and encourage the use of multiple sources of information. Have students share their learning in a variety of ways.

The Listening Walk

Written by: Paul Showers
Published by: HarperCollins Publishers

Major Topics:

Organisms – Humans, Characteristics, Environment, Senses
Sound – Pitch, Sources

National Science Education Content Standards (1996)

Life Science

- The Characteristics of Organisms
- Organisms and Their Environments

Physical Science

- Position and Motion of Objects

Summary:

In this story a girl, her father, and her dog take a walk. This is not an ordinary walk; it is a "listening walk." As they walk around the block, through the city, in the park, and near the pond, she discovers that there are sounds of various types all around her. She listens to the sounds of the people, vehicles, animals, weather and machines; they all make different sounds. The girl realizes that when we are still and quiet, sounds can be heard everywhere.

Science Concept Map

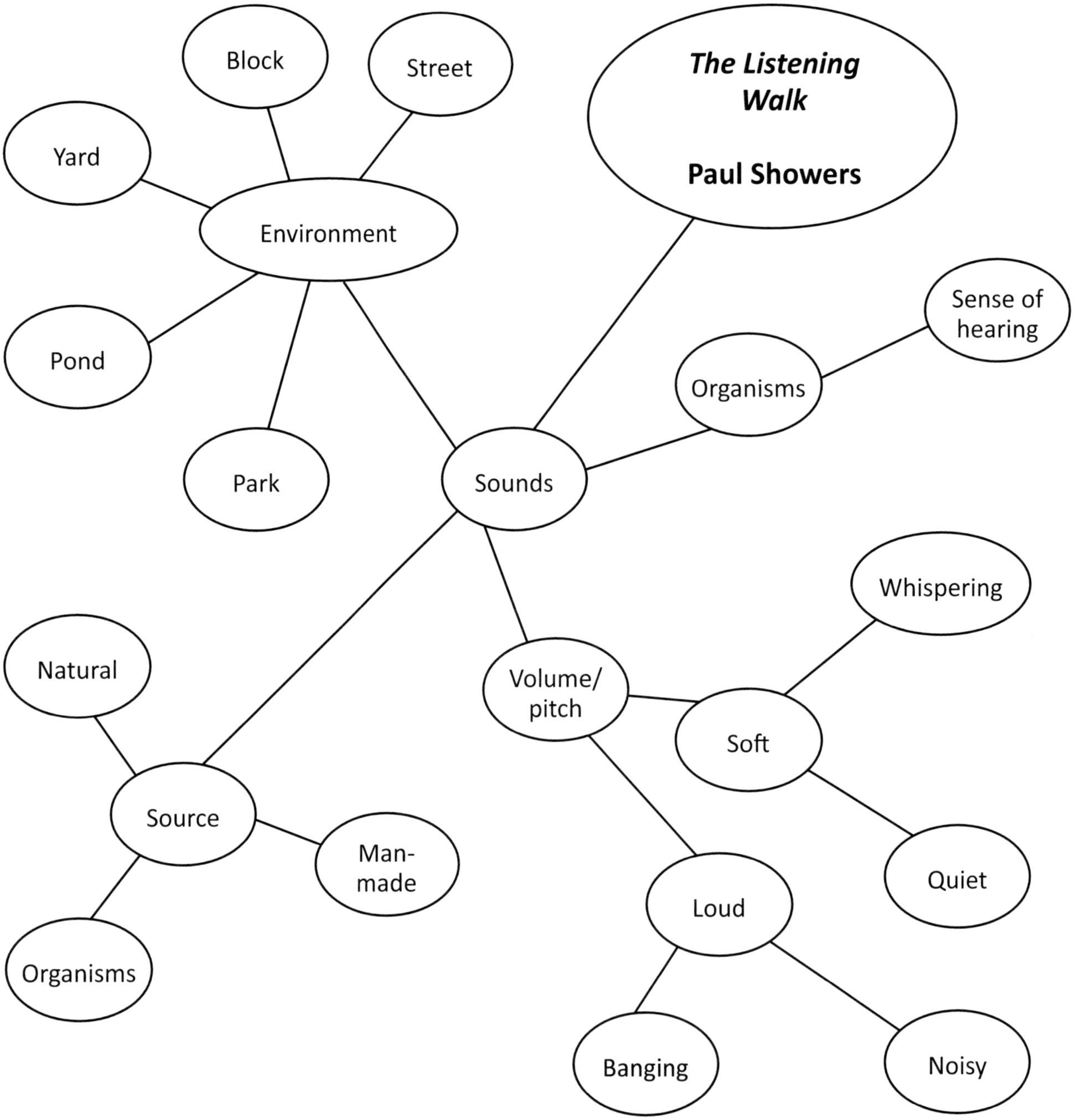

Thinking Questions Based on Bloom's Taxonomy: *The Listening Walk*

1. **Knowledge:**
   According to the girl, what is a "listening walk"? Who went on the walk? Where did she visit on the listening walk? What sounds did she hear? What or who made sounds on her walk?

2. **Comprehension:**
   Why was it important for the girl to keep still and/or quiet on her listening walk? They visited several places on their walk. What words did she use to describe the sounds she heard? Which human sense did they use the most in the walk? What other senses did they use?

3. **Application:**
   Suppose the girl had taken the listening walk at night. Compare and contrast the sounds you think she would hear at night with the sounds she heard during the day walk. List and describe the sounds you hear when you sit quietly in your classroom. List and describe the sounds you hear when everyone is working in class. Where could you go in the school to hear different types of sounds? At home, what types of sounds would you hear? How would you adapt to a world with no sound? Find a way to communicate with someone without making any sounds.

4. **Analysis:**
   Where did they hear the loudest sounds? Where did they hear the softest sounds? Classify the sounds the girl heard in different places into different groups. (e.g., loud or soft sounds, man-made sounds or natural sounds, human sounds or animal sounds). Compare and contrast the different sounds the girl heard in the park, on the street, and in her neighborhood.

5. **Synthesis:**
   Why did the girl name her walk the "listening walk"? Explain your thinking.
   How do we use sounds to communicate with each other? Why are sounds important to the world? To most humans? Explain. Humans have five senses; what other types of "walks" could you take to observe the world around you?

6. **Evaluation:**
   Think of the sounds you hear everyday. Which sound is the most important to you? Which sounds do you like the most? Which sound is the most irritating? Explain your answers. Would you like to go on a "listening walk"? Why or why not?

Follow-Up Activities

The Listening Walk

- Have students go on a "listening walk" at school, outside, or at home. Observe what they hear and collect data. Keep ongoing lists and visual images of sounds in different locations. Develop a book or skit describing the sounds from your own listening walk.
- Experiment with sound using a variety of materials. Collect materials in and out of the classroom. Make an instrument using the different materials. As you create your instrument, consider various pitches and tones it can make. Find sounds in the real world that are similar to the instrument's sounds. Research uncommon sounds one would hear in different places and different parts of the world. Try to recreate the sounds using more common items. Share research findings with the class.
- Make a list of words used to describe sound. Write a story, poem, or song using as many sound words as possible.
- Research the world of the deaf including the causes of deafness, sign language, and other related topics. Share information found in written, visual or artistic ways. For example dramatize a short skit without using any sounds. Make sure to be respectful and sensitive to those who are unable to hear.
- Investigate the characteristics, parts, and function of the ear. Develop a visual and written project sharing this information.
- Bring in different items from home that make different sounds, like various shoes or hardware. Have students compare and contrast the sounds, and consider pitch, vibration, and volume.
- Research other specific interests, curiosities, and basic information about environment, organisms, senses, and sound. Provide and encourage the use of multiple sources of information. Have students share their learning in a variety of ways.

The Lorax

Written and Illustrated by: Dr. Seuss
Published by: Random House

Major Topics:

Environment – Changes, Issues
Organisms – Animals/Humans, Plants, Basic Needs, Behaviors, Habitats
Resources – Natural, Man-Made

National Science Education Content Standards (1996)

Life Science

- The Characteristics of Organisms
- Organisms and Their Environments

Science in Personal and Social Perspectives

- Types of Resources
- Changes in the Environment

Summary:

In this tale, the Once-ler shares of his past and warns a boy of how pollution and misuse of natural resources can affect the survival of all plants and creatures. A long time ago in a "glorious place," the Once-ler discovered that he could make a fortune using the tufts of the Truffula Trees by making Thneeds, "a fine-something-that-all-people-need." Thneeds become something everyone seems to "need" and buy. The Lorax, a creature who speaks for all the living things in the forest, warns the Once-ler that his actions will eventually destroy the environment and cause the creatures to leave. It was not until the last tree had been cut down, all the creatures had been forced from the forest, and his business closed that the Once-ler realized he should have listened to the warning of the Lorax. The Once-ler's greed and carelessness destroyed the environment and the natural habitat of the creatures. But hope stills remains, as the Once-ler passes the one remaining Truffula Tree seed to the boy and challenges him to rebuild the forest in hope that the Lorax and other creatures will one day return.

Science Concept Map

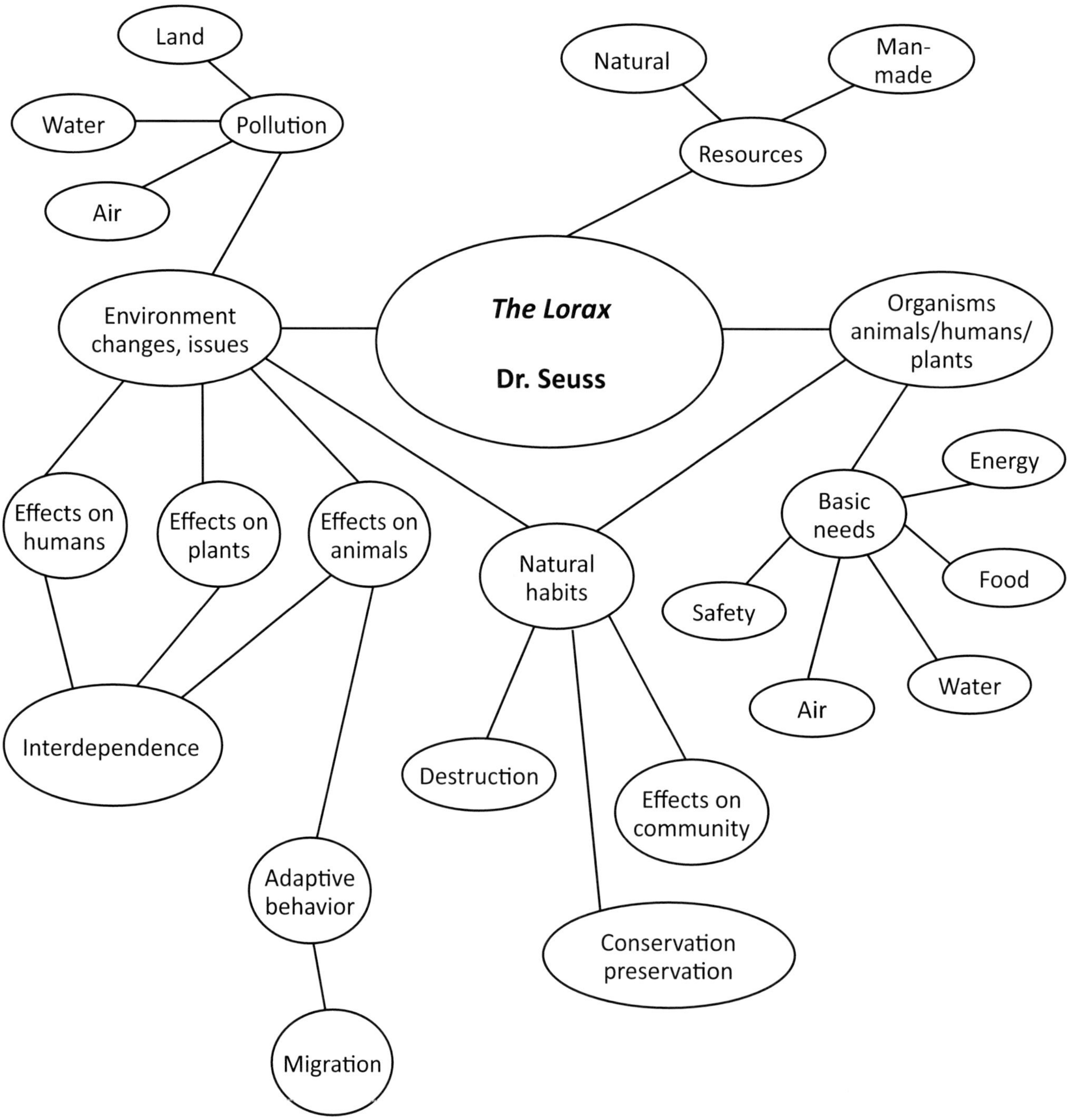

The Lorax

Dr. Seuss

Resources
Natural
Man-made

Environment changes, issues
Pollution
Land
Water
Air
Effects on humans
Effects on plants
Effects on animals
Interdependence
Adaptive behavior
Migration

Organisms animals/humans/ plants
Basic needs
Energy
Food
Water
Air
Safety

Natural habits
Destruction
Effects on community
Conservation preservation

Thinking Questions Based on Bloom's Taxonomy: *The Lorax*

1. **Knowledge:**
   What did the Once-ler find in the "glorious place" at the beginning of the story? What did the Once-ler do in the "glorious place" he found? What did the Once-ler make with the tufts of the Truffula Trees? What warnings did the Lorax give the Once-ler?

2. **Comprehension:**
   Why did the Once-ler not heed the warnings of the Lorax? Why were the Truffula Trees valuable to the Once-ler? To the forest? How was the forest destroyed? How were the creatures and forest harmed as the trees were cut down? What happened to the Bar-ba-loots? Swomee-Swans? Humming-Fish? How did the factory affect the forest? Why did the Lorax warn the Once-ler of the effects of his greed and factory? Why did the Once-ler change his perspective by the end of the story?

3. **Application:**
   What natural resources help us to meet our basic needs? Why do humans cut down trees? What things come from trees? What are reasons that we need to conserve/preserve trees? If humans used resources unwisely and never replenished, what would happen to the Earth's environment? What kinds of things do you buy that are like "thneeds"? How can you do without them?

4. **Analysis:**
   What happened to the "glorious place" as time passed? Classify the direct and indirect effects of the loss of the Truffula Trees. Compare and contrast the forest before and after the Once-ler. What caused the Lorax to "cough, whiff, sneeze, and croak"? Why did the Once-ler give the child a seed at the end of the story? After the child receives the seed, predict what happens next in the story. What did the seed at the end of the story signify? The Lorax spoke on behalf of what in the story?

5. **Synthesis:**
   Why do you think people bought "thneeds" even though they didn't really need them? Why did the Lorax leave the sign "UNLESS" for the Once-ler? Discuss the importance of trees and plants to the existence of all living things. Pretend you were with the Lorax, how would you convince the Once-ler to save the trees, the creatures, and the forest? How could the Lorax and the Once-ler have worked together to meet everyone's needs?

6. **Evaluation:**
The Once-ler used the trees for a business. Do you agree with him? Why or why not? Did the Lorax do all that it could to save the environment? Is cutting down just one tree doing harm? Explain your thinking.

Follow-Up Activities

The Lorax

- Explore environmental issues. Research and investigate resources that are becoming scarce on Earth. Research and investigate animals that are endangered or already extinct. Determine the role of humans in these situations; consider benefits and challenges.

- As cities, towns, and suburbs expand to meet our wants and needs, the natural habitats of animals are destroyed. Pick one situation and create a plan that will allow humans to meet their wants and needs, while at the same time preserving the natural habitat of animals. Share plans with appropriate leadership.

- Look around the classroom, school, and home for things that are made from trees. Research the process. Are there any other natural resources (other than trees) we use regularly?

- Pick any living thing and pretend it is the last one alive of its type. Devise a plan for keeping it from becoming extinct. Create visual and written products.

- Become a Lorax and defend something in the natural world (i.e., an animal, plant, or habitat). Research the cause and present its perspective to a variety of audiences.

- Look at different perspectives of certain environmental issues. Think about the Once-ler and the Lorax; could both sides be “right” at some point? Explain. Publish this analysis in a journal format.

- As a group or as individuals, write a sequel to the story with what the boy does with the seed and its impact on the environment. Perform the sequel to the school community.

- Research other specific interests, curiosities, and basic information about environmental issues, natural resources, and organisms. Provide and encourage the use of multiple sources of information. Have students share their learning in a variety of ways.

The Magic Fan

Written and Illustrated by: Keith Baker
Published by: Voyager Books/Harcourt

Major Topics:

Environment – Changes, Organisms
Technology – Inventions
Weather

National Science Education Content Standards (1996)

Science and Technology
- Understanding about Science and Technology

Science in Personal and Social Perspectives
- Changes in the Environment
- Science and Technology in Local Challenges

Life Science
- Organisms and Their Environments

Earth and Space Science
- Changes in the Earth and Sky

History and Nature of Science
- Science as a Human Endeavor

Summary:

Yoshi, a builder and inventor, has constructed houses, wagons, tables, and fences for the entire village where he lives. When he finds that he has built everything the people need, he does not know what to do next. A magic fan comes to his aid and gives him ideas of what to build next. The magic fan inspires him to build a boat to catch the moon, a kite to look over the world, and a bridge to stretch across the village like a rainbow. The villagers become angry that Yoshi is building things they do not apparently need, until the bridge ends up being the only place where the villagers can stay safe during a destructive tsunami. As they work together to rebuild the village, Yoshi discovers his inspiration to create is not in the magic fan but within himself.

Science Concept Map

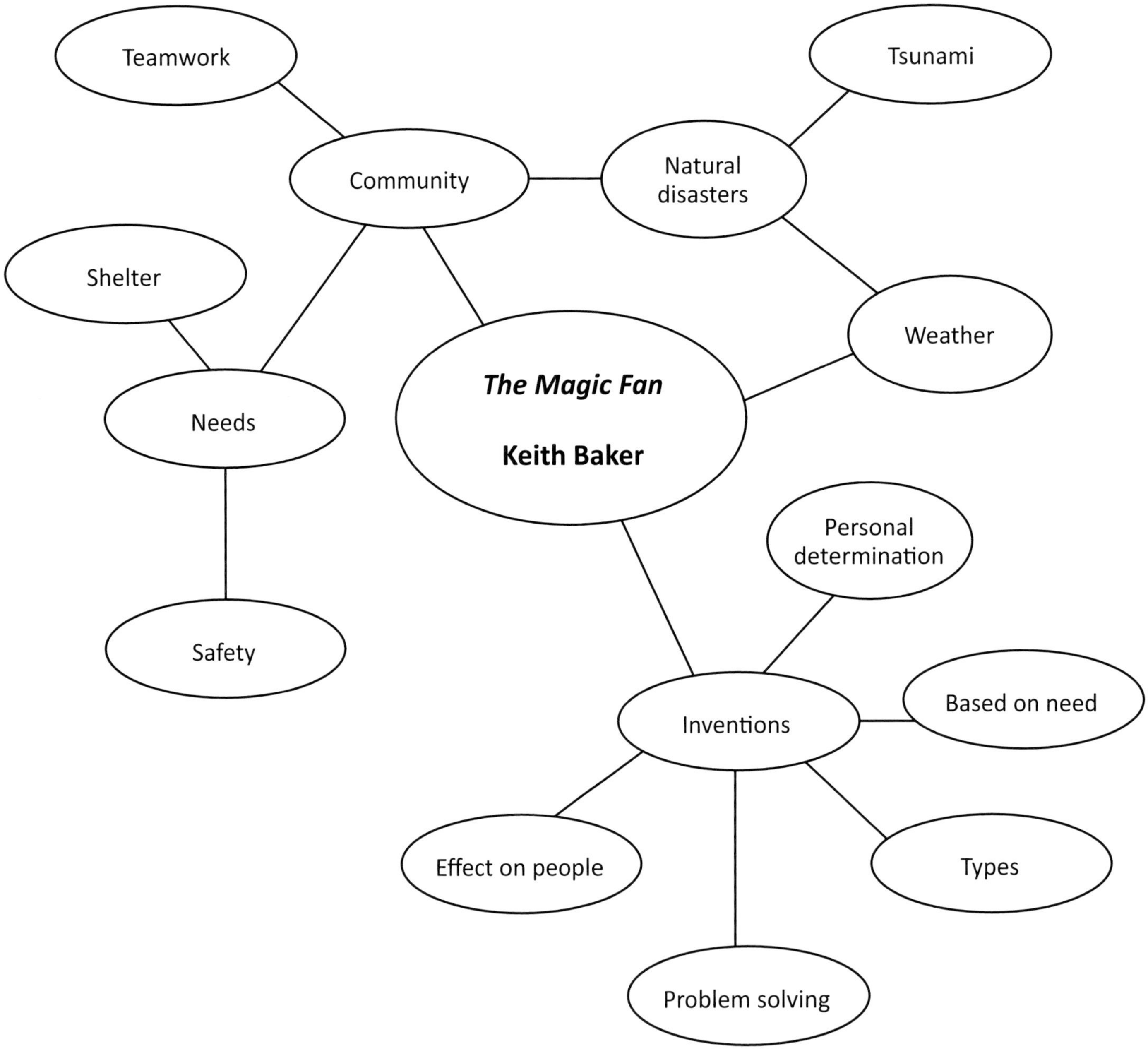

The Magic Fan

Keith Baker

- Community
  - Teamwork
  - Natural disasters
    - Tsunami
    - Weather
  - Needs
    - Shelter
    - Safety
- Weather
- Inventions
  - Personal determination
  - Based on need
  - Types
  - Problem solving
  - Effect on people

Thinking Questions Based on Bloom's Taxonomy: *The Magic Fan*

1. **Knowledge:**
   What is Yoshi's skill/trade? What things did Yoshi build before he found the fan? What was Yoshi's problem? What things did the fan inspire Yoshi to build? What type of extreme weather destroyed the village?

2. **Comprehension:**
   How did Yoshi support the community? How did the people survive the tsunami? Explain why the people became angry with Yoshi. Then after the tsunami, why were the people grateful for Yoshi?

3. **Application:**
   The tsunami was the natural disaster that destroyed the village. Predict and explain what your town would do if it experienced a tsunami or hurricane. Think of an invention that would help you and your family. What technology do you use in your daily lives? Generate a list and explain how you use technology.

4. **Analysis:**
   After the tsunami, what steps did the community take to rebuild? Describe this process. How did Yoshi decide what to build throughout the book? Classify each of Yoshi's new inventions based on their properties and usefulness. Justify your answers. Compare Yoshi's creations to the natural objects he observed on the magic fan. Compare and contrast Yoshi's inventions before and after the magic fan. What was different between his inventions before the magic fan and after?

5. **Synthesis:**
   Imagine you are a villager. What role did Yoshi play in the community? What type of objects would you want Yoshi to create next? How did all of Yoshi's creations, before and after the magic fan, support the village? Why do people invent new things? Where was the "real" magic? Explain your thinking.

6. **Evaluation:**
   Pretend Yoshi is your real friend. What would you want him to create for you? Explain your answer. At first, the village community discouraged Yoshi from building new things. Was this a good choice? Explain. Was it a good choice for Yoshi to create the things the magic fan inspired and the community originally disliked? Justify your answer. Yoshi trusted the magic fan. Would you have trusted it? Why or why not?

Follow-Up Activities

The Magic Fan

- Have students invent and describe an object to improve the quality of life at school, in class, at home, and/or in your community. Explain how this object will help. Create a visual and written product sharing the new invention.

- Research people who have made contributions throughout the history of science and technology. How have their contributions affected our daily lives? Research scientists from the past and today. Develop a guidebook of "inventors."

- Investigate natural disasters (such as Hurricane Katrina of 2005 and Asian Tsunami of 2004). What causes different types of natural disasters? How did the affected communities rebuild? What tools and technology did they use? What types of inventions could have saved communities from destruction?

- Have students reflect and observe their own daily lives. Gather data on the inventions/technology that are used every day and/or on special occasions. Determine the purpose for each and research how they were developed.

- Design and build bridges using different materials. Explore with various structural designs to discover which is the sturdiest in a simulated tsunami. Study the history of bridges and how their construction has progressed over time.

- Research other specific interests, curiosities, and basic information about environmental changes, inventions, technology, and weather. Provide and encourage the use of multiple sources of information. Have students share their learning in a variety of ways.

Make Way For Ducklings

Written and Illustrated by: Robert McCloskey
Published by: The Viking Press

Major Topics:

Organisms — Animals, Basic Needs, Behavior, Habitat, Life Cycle

National Science Education Content Standards (1996)

Life Science

- The Characteristics of Organisms
- Life Cycles of Organisms
- Organisms and Their Environments

Summary:

Mr. and Mrs. Mallard, soon-to-be-parents of baby ducklings, want to find a perfect place to raise their new duck family in the city of Boston. The parent ducks visit several places around town to find a place that is safe and would provide all of the things they needed to make it a good home. Finally, they find a small island in the river to hatch their eggs and to start raising their family. When the ducklings are old enough, Mrs. Mallard, with the help of some policemen and the community in dodging some challenges of city life, takes the ducklings to a new home in the Public Garden, where their needs are even better met.

Science Concept Map

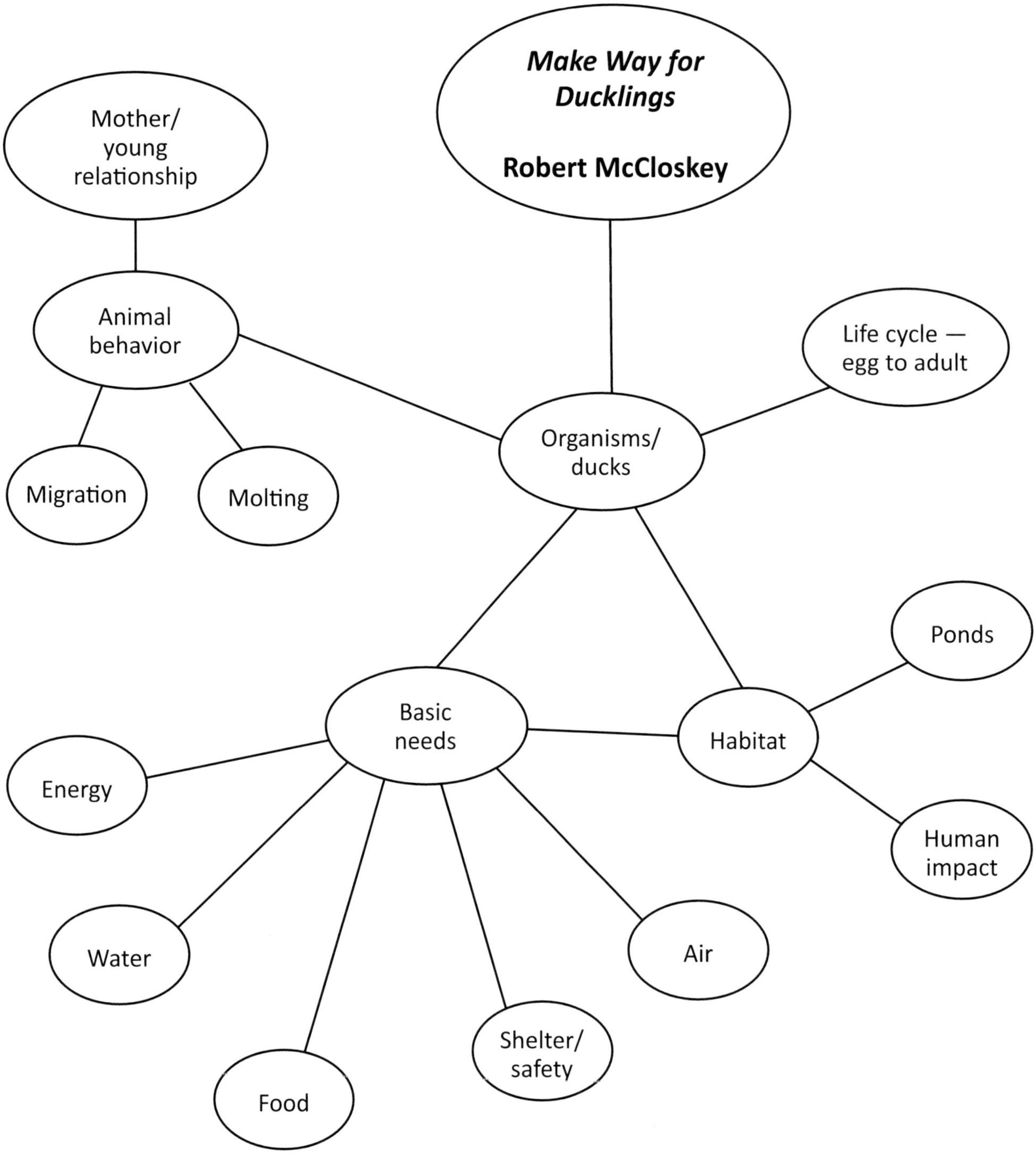

Thinking Questions Based on Bloom's Taxonomy: *Make Way for Ducklings*

1. **Knowledge:**
   What were Mr. and Mrs. Mallard doing as they flew around the city? Name at least two things that Mrs. Mallard did not want in her nesting habitat. From what did the ducklings hatch? What were the dangers the Mallard Family faced in the city? Where did the Mallard Family end up living?

2. **Comprehension:**
   How did the mother duck protect her young? Why did Mrs. Mallard want to make sure that there were no foxes and turtles in her nesting habitat? Why did the Mallards choose the nesting habitat they did? Which foods were naturally found in the habitat? Not naturally? Why did the "strange enormous bird" not speak to the Mallards? Why did they choose the Public Garden as their final habitat?

3. **Application:**
   Are there any habitats around your own home or school that would be "good" for a mallard duck family? What changes would have to be made? How do humans take care of their young? How does your habitat meet your needs?

4. **Analysis:**
   Think about the Mallard Family's habitat in the Public Garden. What are the most important things it provided for the ducks? How did the people affect the duck's habitat? How did the people support the duck's habitat? How did the people not support the duck's habitat? Compare the things in the duck's habitat with things you need in your own habitat as a person. How are these the same? How are they different?

5. **Synthesis:**
   Describe the "perfect" habitat that Mrs. Mallard wanted for her baby ducklings (where, what it is made of, what does it provide, etc.). What could have happened if the mother duck tried to raise her ducklings in the Public Garden? Did the Mallards do a good job picking a habitat? Explain. Why are habitats important for organisms? Explain. How do organisms "choose" their habitat?

6. **Evaluation:**
   Were the people in the story more "helpful" or "harmful" to the ducks? Why? Should humans interfere with animals and their habitat? For example, should people feed animals in a park? Explain.

Follow-Up Activities

Make Way for Ducklings

- Have students draw the different habitats the Mallards explored. Use these drawings to help students understand the differences and similarities of the habitats and why the Mallards made their decisions.
- Visit and observe various natural habitats where ducks and other birds live. Compare and contrast these animal habitats. Determine the impact of humans on these habitats and how the birds' needs are met.
- Have students pretend to be Mrs. Mallard and make a sign to post in the park with some guidelines for how people should behave in a park with baby ducks.
- Research the traditional habitats of the wild animals in your local area. Look at the history of development in their town and the impact of it on the environment. Present their findings in visual and written forms.
- Investigate how people can help protect animal populations in your area. Contact local agencies to learn about current initiatives.
- Invite a veterinarian to come and talk about how to make our environment less dangerous for animals and how we should react when we cross paths with a wild animal.
- Have students imagine living in Boston near the Public Garden. Write an article for the local newspaper telling about the Mallard duck family and how the community can support them and their habitat.
- Research other specific interests, curiosities, and basic information about animals, organisms, and their habitats. Provide and encourage the use of multiple sources of information. Have students share their learning in a variety of ways.

Milo and the Magical Stones

Written and Illustrated by: Marcus Pfister
Published by: North-South Books

Major Topics:

Environment – Changes, Issues
Organisms – Animals, Basic Needs, Behavior, Habitat
Resources – Rocks and Minerals
Weather – Weather Patterns

National Science Education Content Standards (1996)

Life Science

- The Characteristics of Organisms
- Organisms and Their Environments

Earth and Space Science

- Properties of Earth Materials
- Changes in the Earth and Sky

Science in Personal and Social Perspectives

- Types of Resources
- Changes in the Environment

Summary:

On a small mountain island, a group of cliff mice live with having their basic needs met. However, during the winter months, the mice yearn for warmth. To solve this, one of the mice, Milo, finds a special glowing rock deep in the mountain that he uses to warm and light his cave through the cold winter nights. As Milo's friends find out about his discovery, the elder mouse Balthazar warns the mice to be respectful of the mountain and to give something back if you take from it. At this point, two different endings are presented; each epitomizes the notion of being good stewards of the environment. In one ending, the community does not follow the elder Balthazar's advice but becomes greedy and takes more rocks from the mountain than they give back, which causes major erosion. With the other ending, heeding Balthazar's advice, Milo and the mice replenish the mountain after taking what they need for warmth and thus maintain balance.

Science Concept Map

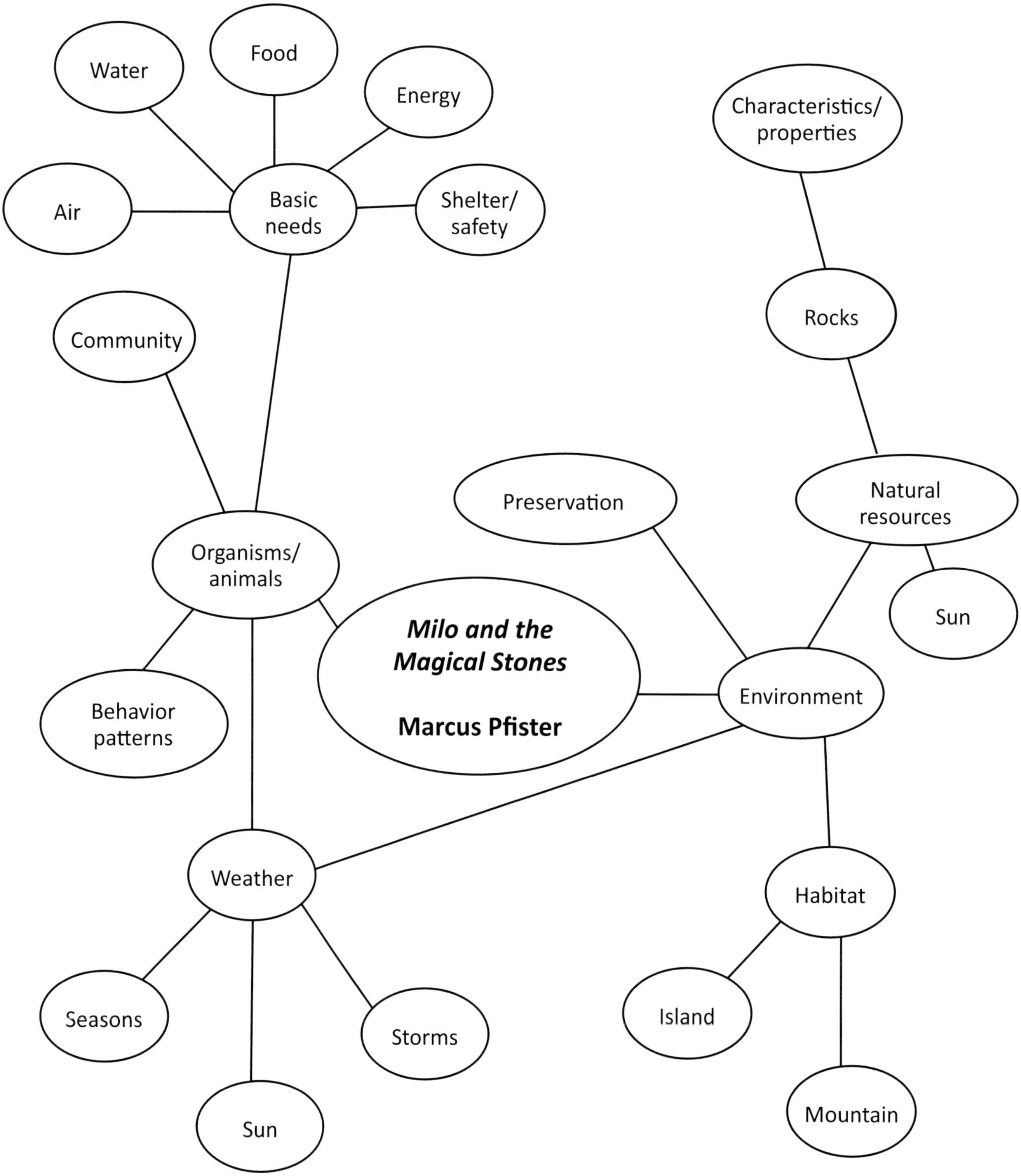

Thinking Questions Based on Bloom's Taxonomy: *Milo and the Magical Stones*

1. **Knowledge:**
   Where did Milo live? What did the mice find to keep themselves warm in the winter? In the happy ending, what did Milo and the mice give back to the mountain? What happened? In the sad ending, what did the mice give back to the mountain? What happened?

2. **Comprehension:**
   Why did Milo and the other mice take the glowing rocks? Describe why the mountain collapsed in the sad ending. How did the mountain habitat meet the needs of the mice?

3. **Application:**
   Think of alternative ways for the mice to be warm in winter. Think of one thing you take/use from the Earth? How do you "give back" to the Earth? Predict what would happen to us if we took all of our natural resources without giving anything back. What kind of things do you do to keep warm in the winter?

4. **Analysis:**
   Which season do you think the mice liked better? Explain your thinking. Explain why Milo chose to replace the magical stone. Differentiate between the two endings. Compare and contrast the events, social aspects, and outcomes of the two endings.

5. **Synthesis:**
   Explain why it was necessary for the mice to take the rocks. In the happy ending, why did the mountain remain standing? Pretend you were the voice of the mountain. How would you help the mice understand the need to replenish the mountain? How does your habitat meet your needs?

6. **Evaluation:**
   Choose the ending you thought was the most appropriate and share your reasons. Is one ending better than the other? Explain. In the world, do humans seem to give or take more from the Earth? Justify your position.

Follow-Up Activities

Milo and the Magical Stones

- Research the importance of natural resources around the globe and in your own community. Discuss resources humans use that are from the Earth. Analyze everyday items to see if they come from the Earth in some way, directly or indirectly.

- Discuss ways to support the environment, including conservation, preservation, and recycling. Investigate plans by various organizations already in place to help give back to the Earth, either at school, at home, or in your town. Create a product (book, video, poster, song, etc.) to teach and share ways to be environmentally friendly. Develop a plan of action for the classroom on a particular issue.

- Have students create a visual and oral presentation to share an alternative way the mice could keep warm in the winter. Consider using other resources, natural and man-made. Develop criteria and evaluate the various plans.

- Brainstorm a list of different kinds of weather. Draw pictures or role-play how people and animals might adapt to each kind of environmental circumstance. Learn more about how various animals prepare for the winter months.

- Explore ways that humans use resources from the Earth to meet basic needs and wants. Justify the use of the resources and develop possible alternative resources.

- Build and simulate Milo's mountain-island home using a variety of Earth materials. Look at the impact of water erosion and structural changes like the mice created in the "sad ending." Experiment with different types of rocks to determine which rocks have the properties which would sustain the environmental changes the best.

- Research other specific interests, curiosities, and basic information about animals, environmental issues, minerals, organisms, rocks, and weather patterns. Provide and encourage the use of multiple sources of information. Have students share their learning in a variety of ways.

Moonbear's Shadow

Written and Illustrated by: Frank Asch
Published by: Aladdin Paperbacks

Major Topics:

Earth's Movement – Shadows, Sun, Clouds

National Science Education Content Standards (1996)

Earth and Space Science

- Objects in the Sky
- Changes in the Earth and Sky

Physical Science

- Light, Heat, Electricity, and Magnetism

Summary:

Bear, the main character in this story, appears to have a problem. His "Shadow" is in the water and scaring away the fish he wants to catch. No matter where he goes or what he does, he cannot get rid of Shadow. He believes he is successful when at noon Shadow disappears. When he awakes from his noon nap, Shadow remains. Bear comes up with a possible solution. He and Shadow make a deal and when Bear goes back to fish (and the sun has moved to a different position), Bear catches a fish and sees that Shadow held up his end of the deal!

Science Concept Map

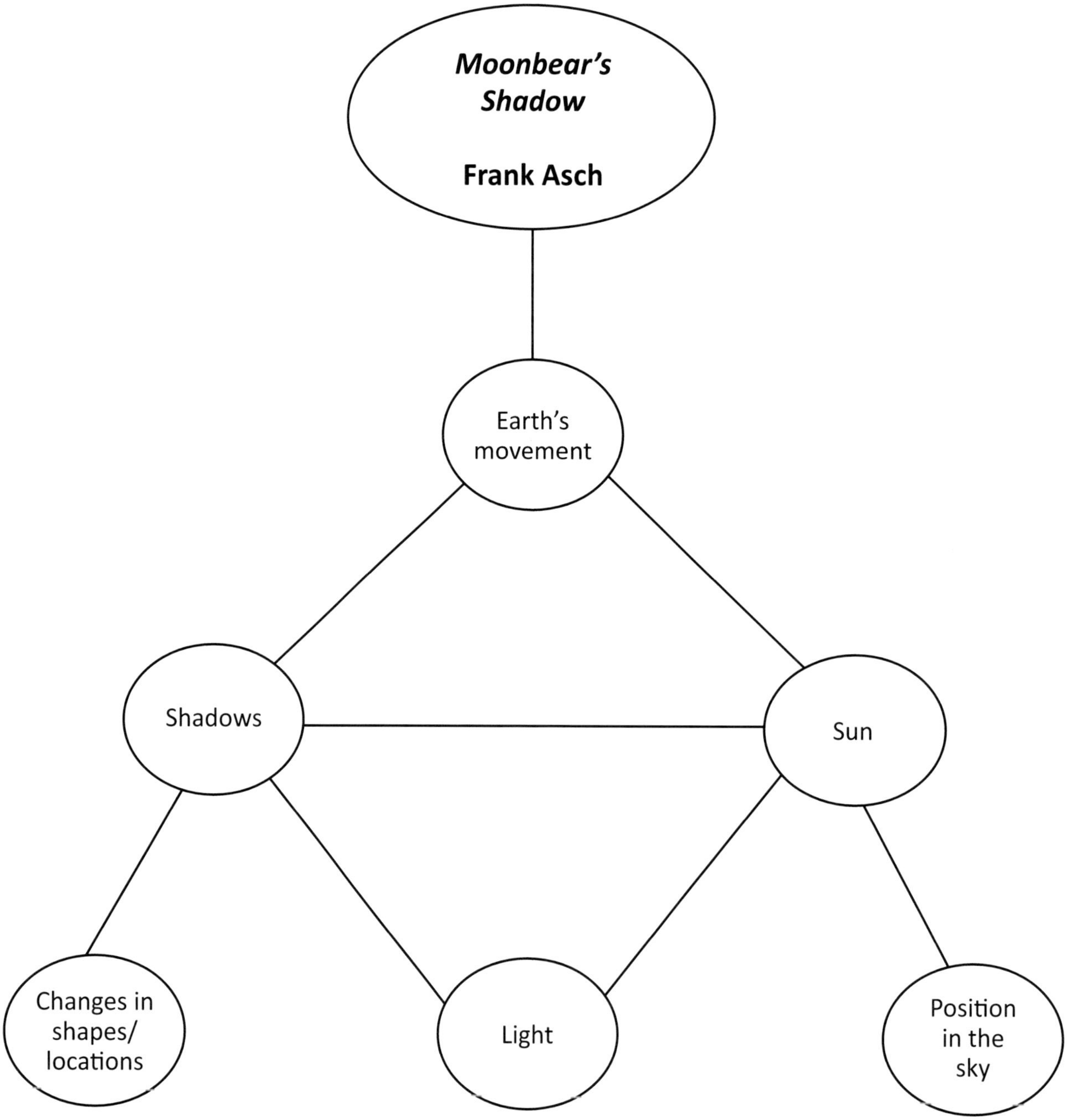

Thinking Questions Based on Bloom's Taxonomy: *Moonbear's Shadow*

1. **Knowledge:**
   Throughout the story, what was Bear trying to do? Why did Bear want to get rid of Shadow? What are some of the ways Bear tries to get rid of Shadow? Was Bear successful at getting rid of Shadow? Was Bear able to catch a fish in the story?

2. **Comprehension:**
   Describe Shadow. Does Shadow always look the same? How does Shadow change throughout the book? When is Shadow not with Bear? What thing in the sky was causing Bear to always see Shadow?

3. **Application:**
   Imagine there were two suns. What would happen to Bear's shadow? Look around the classroom. Where do you see shadows? Are there shadows at night? Does your shadow ever leave you? When? Why or why not? How could you get rid of your shadow?

4. **Analysis:**
   What factors contributed to Bear's shadow being in front of him, beside him, and behind him? Compare and contrast Bear's shadow when he was fishing at the pond in the beginning of the book to when he was fishing at the pond at the end of the book. Why had it moved? What factors caused Shadow to go away at noon. Bear tried to get rid of Shadow in many ways. Why could he not get rid of Shadow?

5. **Synthesis:**
   Why are Shadow and Bear together almost all of the time? Predict what will happen to Bear and Shadow the next day. Will they still be together? Construct other effective ways Bear could get rid of Shadow. How was Shadow able to keep the deal with Bear? Explain what causes shadows.

6. **Evaluation:**
   Do you like having a shadow? Why or why not? Do you think Bear should have wanted to get rid of Shadow? Why or why not? What was your favorite way Bear tried to get rid of his shadow? Explain your thinking.

Follow-Up Activities

Moonbear's Shadow

- Go on a "shadow walk." Look for shadows in different places. Collect data on these shadows over time (sizes, locations, etc.) and generalize your findings.

- Have students invent a shadow-making machine. What materials would you need? How would it work? Where could you use it? Why? Create and display prototypes.

- Imagine there are two suns in the solar system. Investigate how this phenomena would affect your shadow. Share your findings in written, oral, and visual formats.

- Pick one stationary object outside. Track this object's shadow throughout the day, a week, and over the season. Collect data in a variety of ways, including measuring, drawing, and photography. What happened to the shadow? Analyze and synthesize the data. Explain student discoveries in a variety of ways. Instead of following an object's shadow, have students follow their own across the course of a day. Have partners trace student shadows in the morning, at noon, and then again in the evening.

- Have students recreate the story from Shadow's perspective. Tell the story as if you were Shadow with Bear following you everywhere. Illustrate the story with accurate representations of where Bear would be throughout the day. Present the story in a creative manner.

- Research other specific interests, curiosities, and basic information about the Earth's movement, shadows, and the Sun. Provide and encourage the use of multiple sources of information. Have students share their learning in a variety of ways.

Mother Earth

Written by: Nancy Luenn
Published by: Aladdin Paperbacks

Major Topics:

Earth – Organisms, Landforms, Resources
Environment – Issues, Conservation, Preservation, Interdependency
Resources – Natural

National Science Education Content Standards (1996)

Earth and Space Science

- Properties of Earth Materials

Science in Personal and Social Perspectives

- Types of Resources
- Changes in the Environment

Summary:

In this book, Mother Earth is described as the giver of the Earth's creatures, nature, and beauty. By creatively comparing each of the Earth's critical parts to parts of an animal's body, the words in the story allow the reader to imagine Earth as a growing body full of life. The book goes further and suggests ways that humans can give back to Mother Earth, such as by planting trees and keeping rivers and streams free of pollution.

Science Concept Map

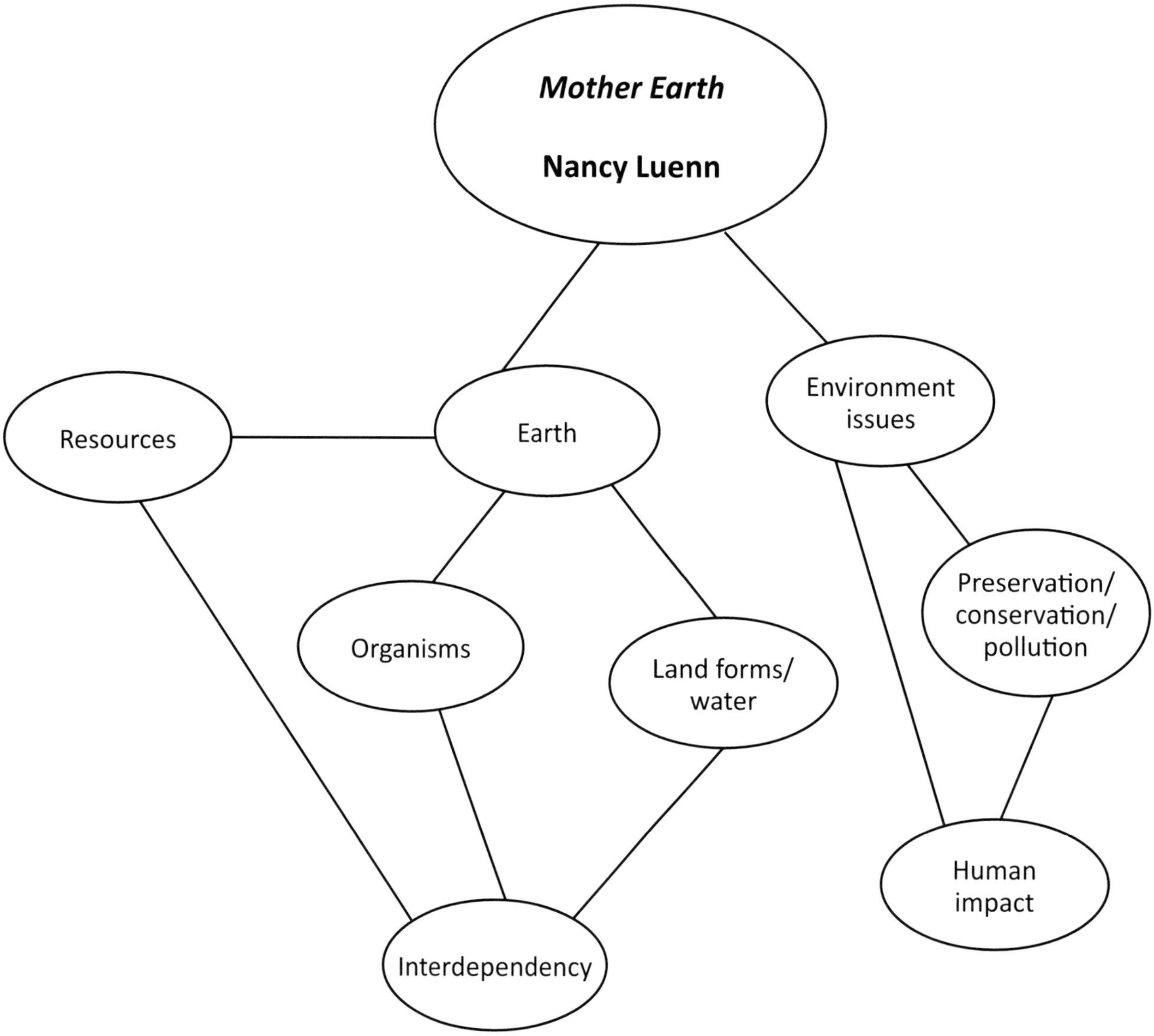

Mother Earth

Nancy Luenn

Resources

Earth

Environment issues

Organisms

Land forms/ water

Preservation/ conservation/ pollution

Human impact

Interdependency

Thinking Questions Based on Bloom's Taxonomy: *Mother Earth*

1. **Knowledge:**
   According to the story, what makes up the Earth? The author compares the Earth to what? Name some ways the Earth is compared to a body.

2. **Comprehension:**
   Describe how the author makes the Earth seem alive. Retell the story in your own words. Discuss how, in the story, people help support the Earth. What gifts can humans give to the Earth?

3. **Application:**
   What resources do you use from the Earth? How do those resources support your daily life? In what ways do you give back to the Earth? What would happen if we used resources from the Earth and never gave back?

4. **Analysis:**
   Determine all of the ways the author compares the different parts of the Earth to parts of a human body. For each comparison, interpret why the author made those relationships. For example, why are trees compared to "her living hair"?

5. **Synthesis:**
   Predict what would happen if the Earth was not taken care of well. Why does the author compare the Earth with a living body? Why is the Earth like a mother? How does the Earth provide for all its organisms? Explain your thinking.

6. **Evaluation:**
   Give your opinion on why we must treat our planet well. Was it a good choice for the author to compare the Earth to a mother's body? Explain your answer. Is it important for humans to give back to the Earth? Why or why not?

Follow-Up Activities

Mother Earth

- Consider the most critical aspects and needs of the Earth. Generate a list of principles humans should live by to respect and protect the Earth. Share their thinking with the school community.
- Discover ways to support a healthy planet. Possibly plan and implement a program for recycling in your classroom and/or school.
- Celebrate and emphasize Earth Day (April 22nd). Discuss and develop ways to give back to the Earth. Research the history of this day and current trends with environmental issues.
- Research and write environmental organizations and ask what they do to help the environment. Determine the purpose of each of these organizations. Compose a proposal to one of the organizations to help your schoolyard be more respectful to the natural environment.
- Dramatize the story of *Mother Earth*. Make the different aspects of the book come alive. Add more information or descriptions if needed.
- Write a class poem comparing a local habitat to a body, like *Mother Earth*. Integrate the critical aspects of the habitat into the story as well as issues relating to the environment. Publish the poem in a variety of ways.
- Research other specific interests, curiosities, and basic information about Earth and environmental issues. Provide and encourage the use of multiple sources of information. Have students share their learning in a variety of ways.

Once I Knew a Spider

Written by: Jennifer Owings Dewey
Published by: Walker & Company

Major Topics:

Organisms – Animals/Humans, Spiders, Basic Needs, Behavior, Habitat, Life Cycle

National Science Education Content Standards (1996)

Life Science

- The Characteristics of Organisms
- Life Cycles of Organisms
- Organisms and Their Environments

Summary:

An expectant mother has the opportunity to observe the daily activities and life cycle of an orb weaver spider that has spun a web outside her window. As her own pregnancy progresses and her baby is born, the young mother witnesses a miracle of nature as she watches the orb weaver spider lay eggs and protect her nest from both prey and weather conditions over a year. After the spiderlings hatch and go on their own way, the mother orb spider dies, and the woman watches how the orb weaver spider's life lives on through future spider generations.

Science Concept Map

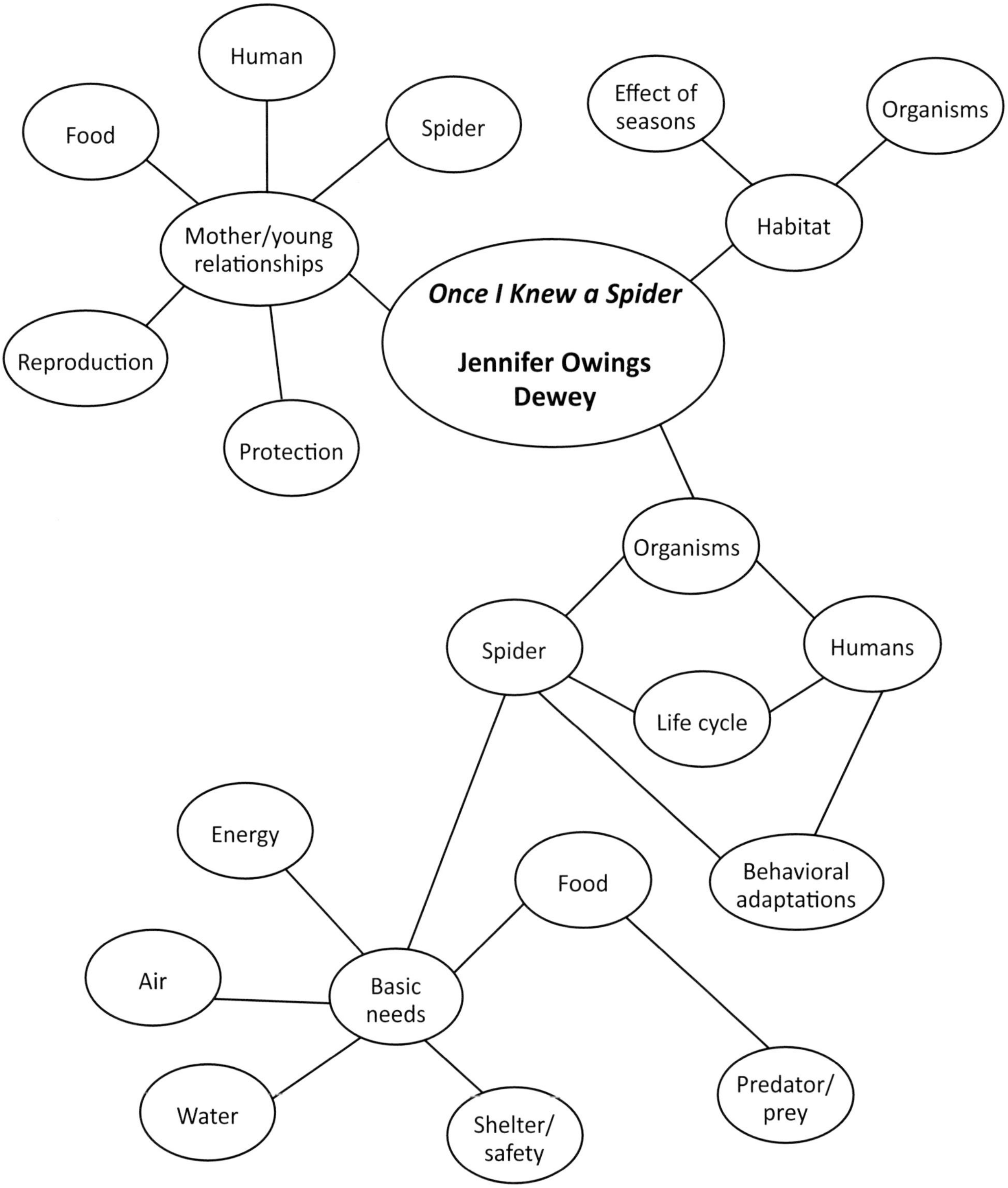

Once I Knew a Spider

Jennifer Owings Dewey

- Mother/young relationships
  - Human
  - Food
  - Spider
  - Reproduction
  - Protection
- Habitat
  - Effect of seasons
  - Organisms
- Organisms
  - Spider
    - Life cycle
    - Behavioral adaptations
    - Basic needs
      - Energy
      - Air
      - Water
      - Shelter/ safety
      - Food
        - Predator/ prey
  - Humans
    - Life cycle
    - Behavioral adaptations

Thinking Questions Based on Bloom's Taxonomy: *Once I Knew a Spider*

1. **Knowledge:**
   What kind of spider was the woman observing? List the predators that threatened the spider's nest. What did the spider do before she died? What did the orb spider build in order to survive?

2. **Comprehension:**
   How was this particular spider more unusual than other spiders? Describe how the spider caught her food. How did the spider adapt to live through each of the seasons? What physical characteristics do spiders have that support how they live?

3. **Application:**
   As a young child, who helps to protect you? Give examples of how parents/guardians and other adults protect and provide for your basic needs. Think of other animals; how do they care for their young? How do other animals create habitats in which to live?

4. **Analysis:**
   Compare and contrast the mother spider to the human mother in the story. Based on the story, what are the basic needs of a spider? How did the spider protect her nest through the seasons?

5. **Synthesis:**
   Based on the story, predict the major events of the baby orb spider's life. Do you think any of the baby spiders will live through the winter? Why or why not? Describe how the spider was able to have her needs met in this environment? Why did the woman think the spider "did well" before she died?

6. **Evaluation:**
   The mother and father in this story choose not to remove the spider from their window. Was this a good choice? What would you have done? Explain. Discuss why you think the spider worked so hard to stay alive.

Follow-Up Activities

Once I Knew a Spider

- Investigate how spiders produce silk and use silk to take care of themselves and their young. Also study how humans use silk as a natural resource.
- Research and chart the life cycle and other interesting information of an ordinary orb weaver spider. Compare and contrast with other types of spiders' life cycles and other animals. How do they survive in their habitats? Become experts on this topic.
- Explore the benefits of spiders in different environments. Look at spiders indigenous to your local area as well as other areas. Study the challenges of spiders in the community.
- Rewrite the story from the mother orb weaver spider's point of view. Consider how she would view the human mother's life and pregnancy.
- Create food chains involving spiders. Study predator/prey relationships. How do other predators catch their food? Create visual representations of the food chains and spiders' roles, predators, and prey.
- Research other specific interests, curiosities, and basic information about organisms and spiders. Provide and encourage the use of multiple sources of information. Have students share their learning in a variety of ways.

The Reason for a Flower

Written and Illustrated by: Ruth Heller
Published by: Penguin Putnam Books for Young Readers

Major Topics:

Organisms – Plants, Basic Needs, Characteristics, Life Cycle
Resources – Natural

National Science Education Content Standards (1996)

Life Science

- The Characteristics of Organisms
- Life Cycles of Organisms
- Organisms and Their Environments

Science in Personal and Social Perspectives

- Types of Resources

Summary:

This dual-purpose book tells about the processes and parts of a flower. It takes the reader on the journey of a flower, from the beginning of its life, starting with pollination and seed movement, to the many possible uses of the flower as various plant products. The poem introduces botany to young readers by including the scientific names and illustrations of the parts and types of flowers.

Science Concept Map

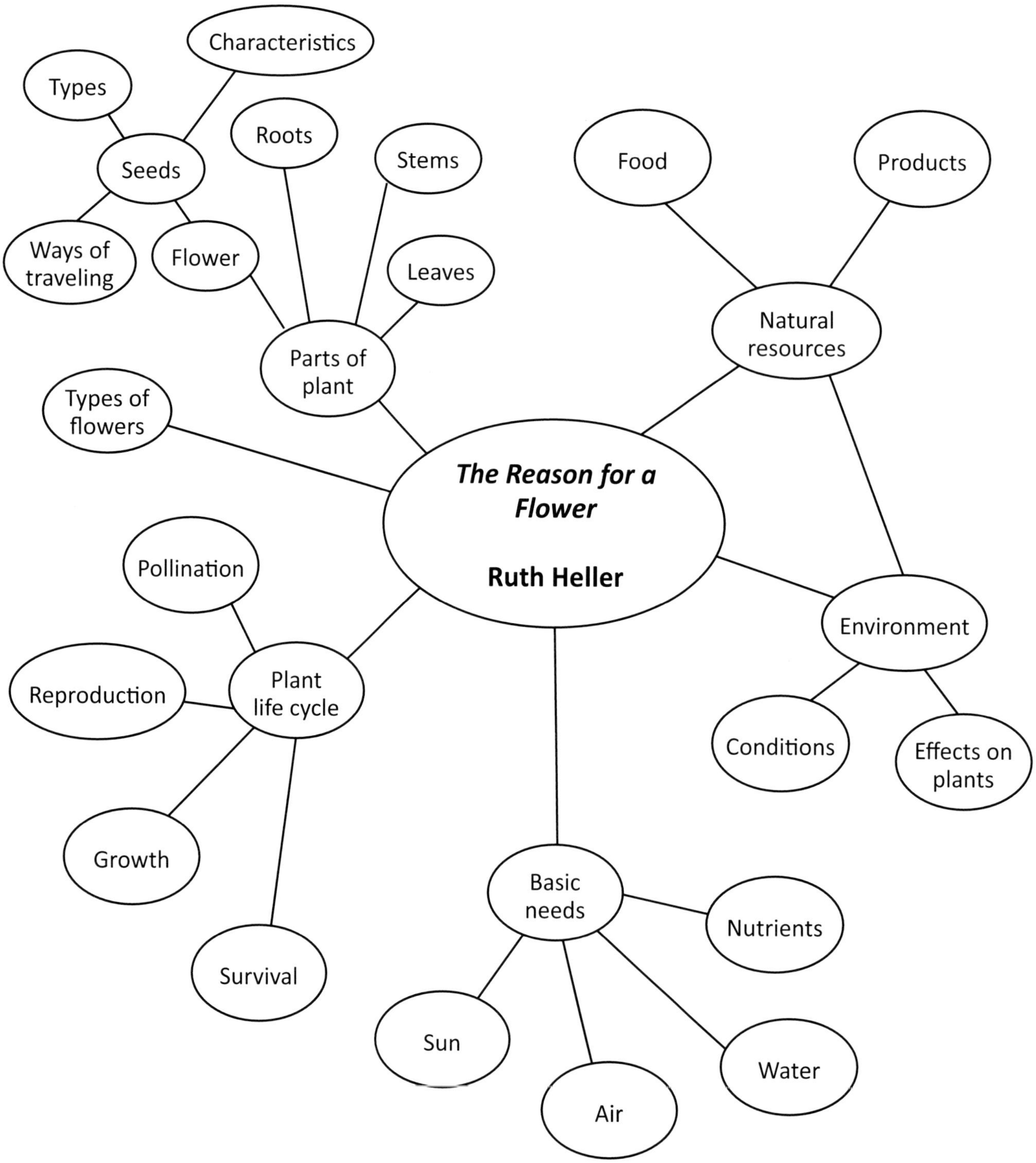

Thinking Questions Based on Bloom's Taxonomy: *The Reason for a Flower*

1. **Knowledge:**
   Name some parts of a plant. What transports pollen in nature? What does a seed become? Name two or more plant products. What things help seeds travel?

2. **Comprehension:**
   Using your own words, retell the story about how a seed becomes a flower. Explain the life cycle of a flower. How did animals help the seed become a flower? How did the weather help? How did the people help? What do seeds need to grow and thrive?

3. **Application:**
   Model with your body the ways that pollen and/or seeds travel. Categorize what parts of plants you use. Think of plant-based resources. Categorize them based on the parts of plants used. Identify the parts of a flower and discuss what role each part plays in the plant.

4. **Analysis:**
   What roles do animals and the environment play in the life cycle of a plant? Predict what would happen to seeds if there was no wind or animals. Compare and contrast plants that are herbivorous and carnivorous. Consider the plant characteristics.

5. **Synthesis:**
   Explain the reason for a flower. Summarize how animals, plants, and the environment are interdependent. Imagine if a plant did not have one of its body parts. Describe what would happen and how that body part's purpose would be replaced. Why are seeds and flowers important to humans?

6. **Evaluation:**
   If you were a bee, would you help pollinate the flowers? Why or why not? What is your favorite part of the plant? Why?

Follow-Up Activities

The Reason for a Flower

- Investigate plants. Dissect a seed, a grown plant, and a flower. Use a variety of tools to make observations. Label the parts and determine the function of each part. Compare and contrast the different plant parts.
- Develop a seed collection from around the schoolyard or from various seed packets. Make observations about the seeds. Compare and contrast the different seeds gathered. Pay close attention to their physical characteristics. Determine how these relate to the adult plant.
- Research and investigate how certain plant products are made. Use the resources from the book as a starting point. Study current trends and issues relating to plant products. Create a diagram or flowchart of the process. Share findings with the class in a variety of ways.
- Observe various habitats and their flowering plants around the school yard or study some brought in from home or a nursery. Compare and contrast different flowers and note the physical characteristics of differing flowering plants. Synthesize the data collected to generalize information about flowers.
- Invent a product made from a plant that would be useful to humans and the Earth. Consider the parts used and present reasons why the invention is important to society.
- Research other specific interests, curiosities, and basic information about organisms, plants, and resources. Provide and encourage the use of multiple sources of information. Have students share their learning in a variety of ways.

Rocks in My Pockets

Written by: Marc Harshman and Bonnie Collins
Published by: Cobblehill Books

Major Topics:

Organisms – Humans, Basic Needs, Behavior, Habitat
Earth – Materials - Rocks, Properties
Resources – Natural
Weather – Effects, Types

National Science Education Content Standards (1996)

Earth and Space Science

- Properties of Earth Materials
- Changes in the Earth and Sky

Science in Personal and Social Perspectives

- Types of Resources
- Changes in the Environment
- Science and Technology in Local Challenges

Physical Science

- Properties of Objects and Materials

Life Science

- Organisms and Their Environments

Summary:
The Woods Family lived on the highest point of the mountain, where the strong winds constantly blew. The family had little food and few other resources, but had plenty of rocks. The rocks became a critical part of their lives. They used the rocks to play, to keep warm, and most importantly to keep in their pockets to prevent from being blown away. Their rocks eventually become shiny and beautiful from being used in so many ways. When city folks come from far away to purchase the beautiful stones, the Woods Family discovers an easier life. And though others presume to be able to find these special stones, the beauty of the stones only comes from the hard work and use of the stones by the Woods Family.

Science Concept Map

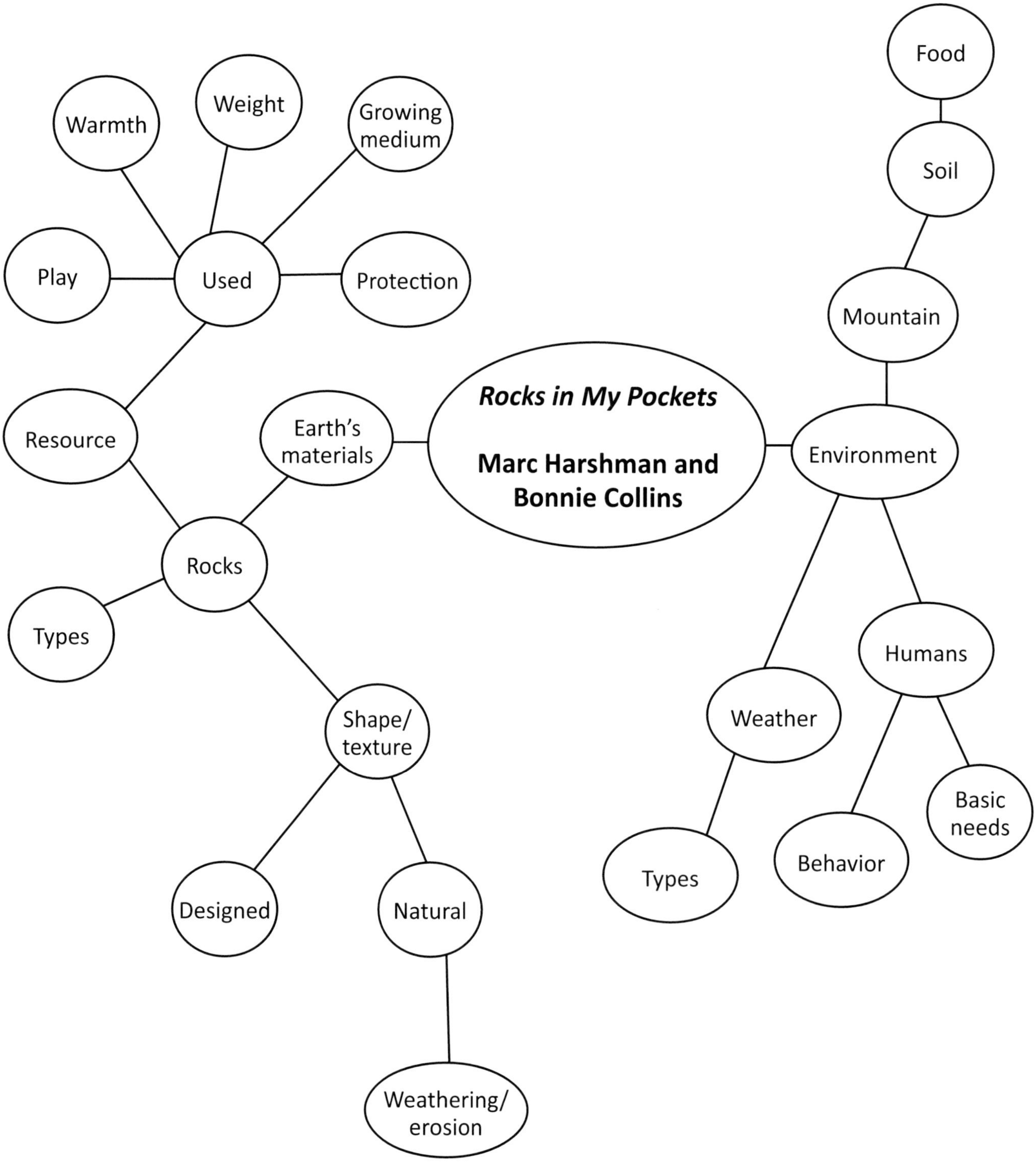

Thinking Questions Based on Bloom's Taxonomy: *Rocks in My Pockets*

1. **Knowledge:**
   Where did the Woods Family live? What was the weather like on the mountaintop? What Earth resource did they use on a daily basis for many purposes? List the ways the Woods Family used rocks in their daily lives.

2. **Comprehension:**
   Why was the Woods Family only able to grow knee-high corn and walnut-sized potatoes? Explain why the Woods Family carried rocks in their pockets. How did the rocks help the family? How did the Woods Family make the rocks so shiny and special? How did the Woods Family's life change after they sold some rocks? What things did not change? What is the effect of the wind on the family?

3. **Application:**
   Select another natural object, other than rocks (e.g., wood, soil). Think of various ways you can use this object to help meet your basic needs. In nature, how do rocks change shape and texture? Aside from the way the Woods Family used the rocks, what are some other uses of rocks?

4. **Analysis:**
   Compare and contrast how the Woods Family and the people from the city used the rocks in the story. Why do you think there are so many rocks on the windy mountainside? Give examples of events that affected the shape and texture of the rocks. Relate your family life to the Woods Family life. What are the similarities and differences? Why did the "city folks" not like the rocks they took from the mountain?

5. **Synthesis:**
   How does weather impact the Woods Family? Predict how the Woods Family's life would be different if they lived on flat land instead of on the windy mountain. How did the rocks impact the Woods Family's life? How do you use natural resources to help you in your everyday life?

6. **Evaluation:**
   In your opinion, do you think Father Woods should have told the "city folks" where to get rocks? Why or why not? Would you have chosen to sell the rocks? Explain your thinking. Is it appropriate for the Woods Family to use the rocks from the mountains as much as they do? Explain.

Follow-Up Activities

Rocks in My Pockets

- Collect different types of rocks from around your school, home, and neighborhood. Sort the rocks based on shape, size, and texture. Classify the rocks scientifically into sedimentary, igneous, and metamorphic rocks using scientific processes and research.

- Take a walk around the school. Look for signs of erosion. Categorize the causes of erosion (wind, water, or another force). Determine ways to prevent erosion.

- Investigate natural phenomena caused by or involving rocks. For example, study the Grand Canyon or major avalanches in mountain regions across the world. Consider the physical causes, implications, and significance of the event. Create visual and written products sharing the research.

- Research the historical uses of rocks. Experiment with rocks as a way to contain heat. Determine the best rocks to conserve heat. Explore other purposes as well.

- Find places around the world that are overall more windy than where you live. How does the wind affect those communities? Study economic, physical, social, and cultural implications.

- Create a dramatization of how the Woods Family uses "those mighty handy rocks." Add other creative uses to the story.

- Design a garden using different types of growing medium. Experiment with rocky soil like that of the Woods's mountain home and other more fertile soil. Grow plants in each medium to study the impact it has on growth.

- Research other specific interests, curiosities, and basic information about organisms, humans, Earth's materials, and weather. Provide and encourage the use of multiple sources of information. Have students share their learning in a variety of ways.

The Sky Tree: Seeing Science Through Art

Written and Illustrated by: Thomas Locker
with Candace Christiansen
Published by: HarperCollins Publisher

Major Topics:

Earth's Movement – Seasons
Organisms – Plants, Basic Needs, Behavior, Life Cycle, Habitat
Weather – Types, Effects

National Science Education Content Standards (1996)

Earth and Space Science

- Changes in the Earth and Sky

Life Science

- The Characteristics of Organisms
- Life Cycles of Organisms
- Organisms and Their Environments

Summary:

A single tree stands on a hill and undergoes many changes as the seasons progress. Its leaves flourish in the summer, change colors in the autumn, fall off in the winter, and bud once again in the spring. The tree's changes are illustrated through Locker's oil paintings, as he uses lyrical prose to express the changes in the tree and its surrounding environment. Locker also provides questions for the readers to explore reactions to the paintings.

Science Concept Map

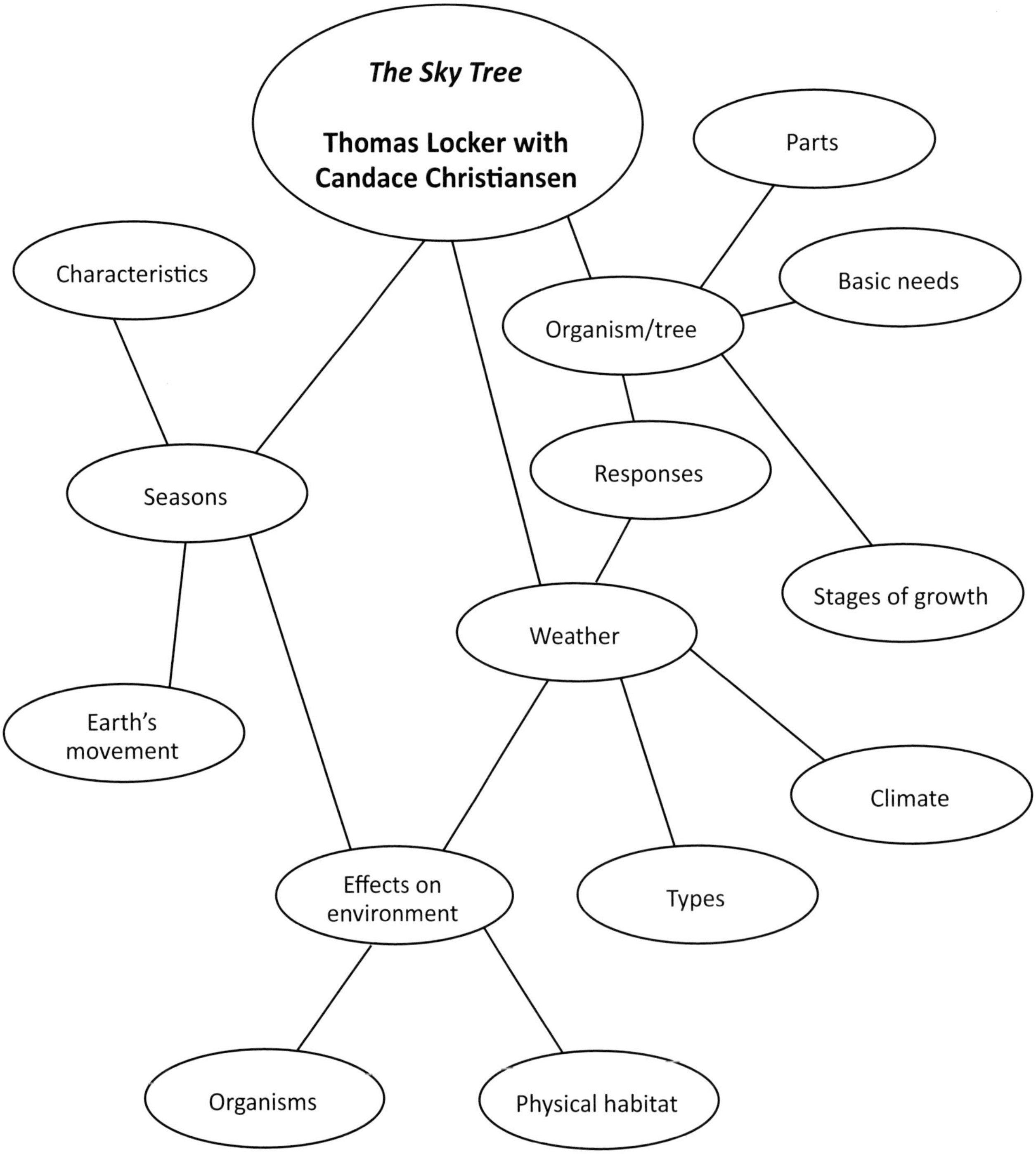

The Sky Tree

Thomas Locker with Candace Christiansen

- Seasons
  - Characteristics
  - Earth's movement
  - Effects on environment
- Weather
  - Responses
  - Climate
  - Types
  - Effects on environment
    - Organisms
    - Physical habitat
- Organism/tree
  - Parts
  - Basic needs
  - Responses
  - Stages of growth

Thinking Questions Based on Bloom's Taxonomy: *The Sky Tree: Seeing Science Through Art*

1. **Knowledge:**
   What seasons did the tree and animals experience? What types of weather occurred in the story? What happened to the tree throughout the story? What did the leaves do throughout each season? Which animals were affected by the seasons?

2. **Comprehension:**
   Discuss the different seasons and how the tree was affected. Explain what the animals did to prepare for each season. Explain what happened to the environment around the tree during each season. How does the river affect the tree?

3. **Application:**
   Think about home or your schoolyard and give examples of other things in nature that change with the seasons. Predict what would happen if this tree was in Antarctica. How do you as a person change during each season?

4. **Analysis:**
   Compare and contrast how the tree looked and behaved throughout the years. Compare and contrast the environment around the tree during the different seasons (sky, weather, other plants, or animals). What things indicated the seasons were changing? Categorize the signs of seasonal changes (weather, animal, plant, and landforms) by season.

5. **Synthesis:**
   Why did the tree change throughout the seasons? Explain. Hypothesize what would happen to the tree if there were no seasons. How are the weather and the environment connected and interdependent? Think about a specific habitat, the organisms, and other conditions.

6. **Evaluation:**
   Give your opinion on why the book is named *Sky Tree*. Which season is your favorite season? Explain. Recommend the season that you think is the best for humans. Which season do you think is best and the worst for this tree? Justify your thinking.

Follow-Up Activities

The Sky Tree: Seeing Science Through Art

- Research coniferous and deciduous trees. Study the differences/similarities including physical properties, responses, and where each type grows. How do changes in seasons impact each type? Have students create a product to show the scientific findings.

- Have students design and create a visual product of a scene from a season of their choice. Include things from the environment that would fit appropriately based on the seasonal climate and changes. Provide a written description to elaborate how each picture represents the given season.

- Adopt a tree and observe it during the school year. Collect and record data in a science journal or on a class observation bulletin board. Create a "Sky Tree" in your class where students collect and share ongoing data from outside.

- Create a similar book using something from nature outside your classroom. Observe what you choose (tree, animal, plant, etc.) all year long to collect data for the project.

- Have students conduct research to learn about how an animal of interest survives and adapts to the different seasons. Share research findings by creating a poster or giving a presentation with visual aids.

- Have students pretend to be a tree and write about what life is like throughout a year. What do you do? How do you feel? What do you think about? How do you change as time passes? Have students pick different environments for the tree, such as the Alaskan mountains or the Hawaiian tropics.

- Research other specific interests, curiosities, and basic information about Earth's movement, weather, and plants/trees. Provide and encourage the use of multiple sources of information. Have students share their learning in a variety of ways.

Snowballs

Written and Illustrated by: Lois Ehlert
Published by: Scholastic, Inc.

Major Topics:

Resources – Natural, Man-made
Earth's Movement/Weather – Snow, Water Cycle
States of Matter

National Science Education Content Standards (1996)

Earth and Space Science

- Changes in the Earth and Sky

Physical Science

- Properties of Objects and Materials

Science and Technology

- Abilities to Distinguish Between Natural Objects and Objects Made by Humans

Summary:

When snow comes, a snow family is built and decorated using a variety of materials that have been collected, such as seeds, buttons, and scarves. Eventually, the sun comes out, changing the frozen water to liquid water, and melts the snow family away. This dual-purpose book offers information on types of materials the narrator uses to form the snow family, as well as general information about snow and its characteristics.

Science Concept Map

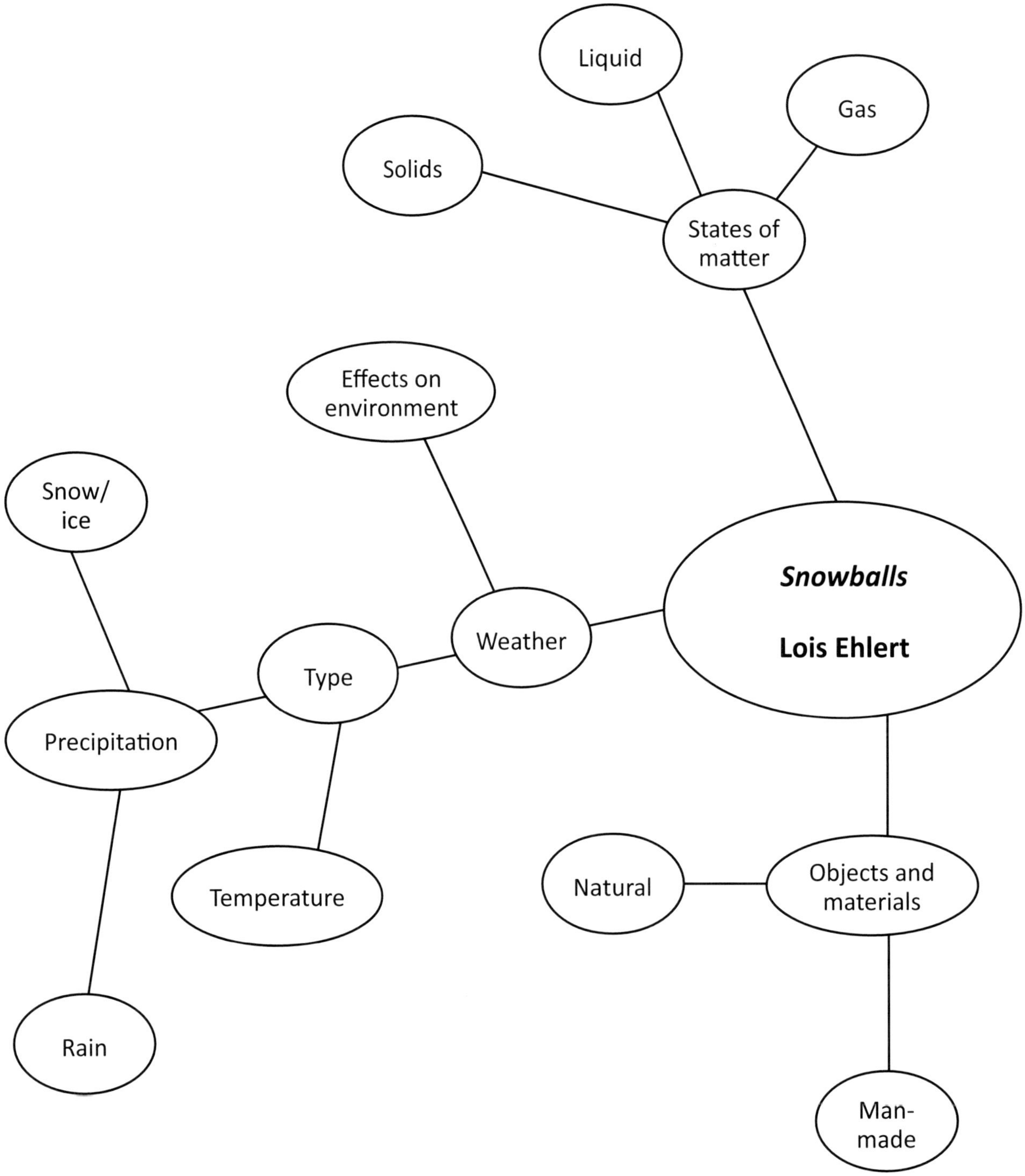

Liquid

Gas

Solids

States of matter

Effects on environment

Snow/ ice

Snowballs

Lois Ehlert

Weather

Type

Precipitation

Temperature

Natural

Objects and materials

Rain

Man-made

Thinking Questions Based on Bloom's Taxonomy: *Snowballs*

1. **Knowledge:**
   What was used to make the snow family? What happened to make the snow family disappear? Name and describe some items used to decorate the snow family.

2. **Comprehension:**
   Explain how the author collected all of the "stuff" at the beginning of the story. What was the weather like when the snow family was made? Describe how each member of the snow family looked when they were newly made and after the sun came out. How did the birds react to the snow coming?

3. **Application:**
   What else could you or the characters in the book create using the same materials that were used to make the snowman? When are you most likely able to build a snow family? How does the weather change where you live throughout the year? If it snows, what do you do? If it rains, what do you do? If it is sunny, what do you do?

4. **Analysis:**
   Explain how the sun affected the snow family. Classify the materials used to make the snow family by natural and man-made resources. Why did it snow? Why did the snow family melt?

5. **Synthesis:**
   How could you prevent the snow family from melting? Name other things that temperature affects in similar ways like the snow. How does weather impact the environment? Think about the habitat, organisms, and social changes.

6. **Evaluation:**
   In your opinion, when making a snow person, which would be best to use: natural or man-made materials? Why? Which is your favorite snow family member? Why?

Follow-Up Activities

Snowballs

- Design an experiment to show property changes of water. Create different ways to freeze, melt, and evaporate water. Observe the changes and conditions needed for the changes. Continue experimenting with other liquids. Do all liquids freeze and evaporate in the same amount of time? Gather, analyze, and synthesize the data.

- Make snow people out of finely crushed ice. Place the creations outside on a sunny day and graph how long it takes for each individual snow person to melt. Try this during at least three different seasons throughout the year. Determine ways to slow down the melting process.

- Keep track of the temperature over the course of the school year. Consider how temperature causes changes in the environment. Look at plants on your school campus and the behavior of people and other animals.

- Research and investigate the different uses for frozen water and liquid water in society and on Earth today and in the past. Look at the importance of water as well as implications of droughts. Create a presentation to share information.

- Have students write and perform a skit/play about the snow family. Show changes based on the weather and in the environment. Add additional conditions to change the snow family's life.

- Research other specific interests, curiosities, and basic information about weather, states of matter, and resources. Provide and encourage the use of multiple sources of information. Have students share their learning in a variety of ways.

The Snowy Day

Written and Illustrated by: Ezra Jack Keats
Published by: Scholastic, Inc.

Major Topics:

Earth's Movement – Seasons, Winter, Changes
Organisms – Humans, Behavior, Habitat
States of Matter
Weather – Effects

National Science Education Content Standards (1996)

Earth and Space Science
- Changes in the Earth and Sky

Physical Science
- Properties of Objects and Materials

Life Science
- The Characteristics of Organisms
- Organisms and Their Environments

Summary:
After a snowfall, Peter experiences all of the wonders of a snowy day. From dressing warmly to playing in the snow, Peter takes advantage of all the snowy day has to offer. As his day comes to an end, Peter tries to preserve the snow by putting a snowball in his pocket. To his dismay, inside his warm house, his snowball disappears. That night, he dreams the sun melts all the snow. But as Peter wakes the next morning, he finds there is even more snow.

Science Concept Map

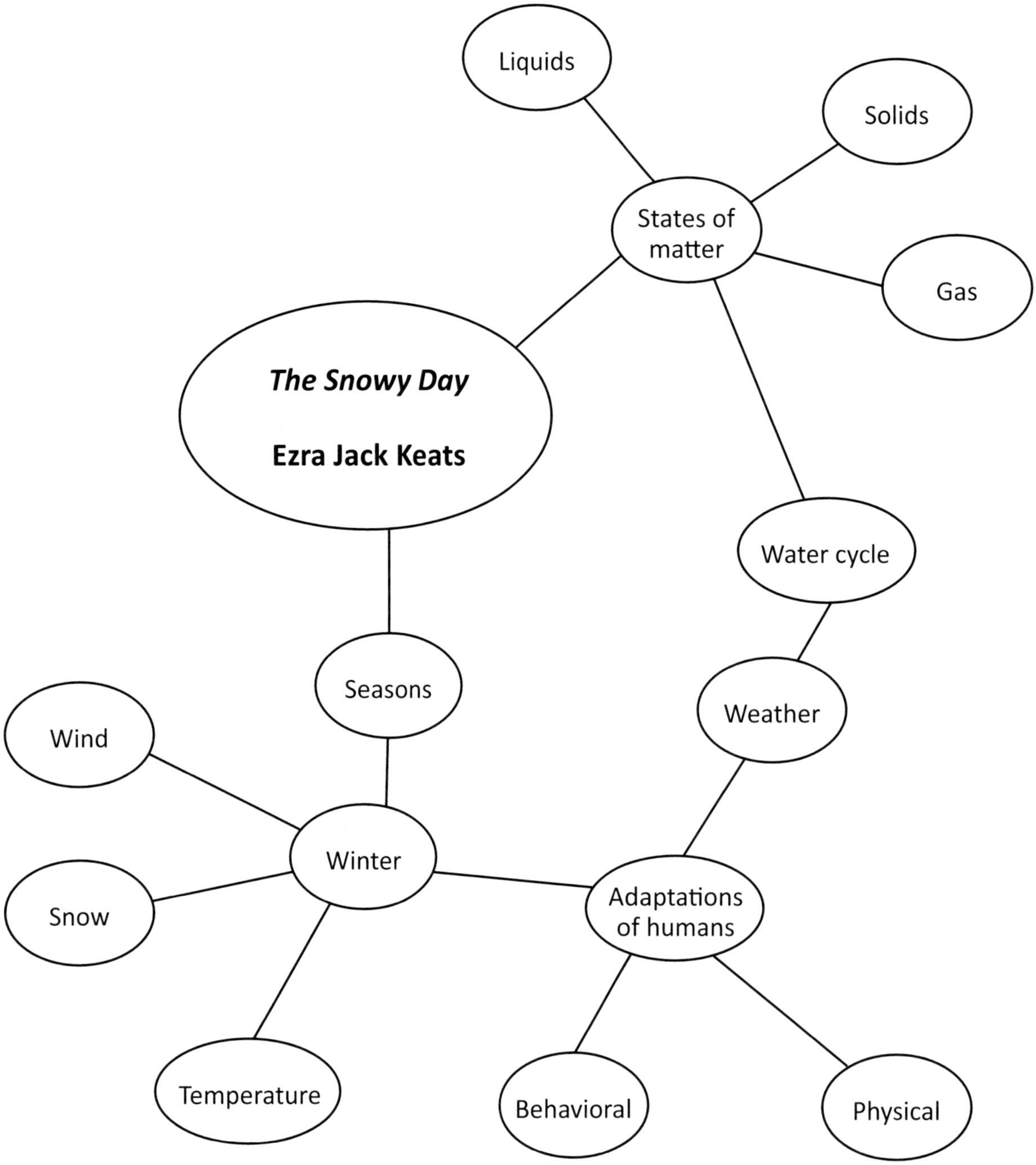

Thinking Questions Based on Bloom's Taxonomy: *The Snowy Day*

1 **Knowledge:**
What did Peter see outside when he woke up in the morning? What did Peter put on to go out in the snow? Name things Peter did outside in the snow. What happened to Peter's snowball that he put in his pocket? Did the sun melt all the snow?

2. **Comprehension:**
Why did Peter put on warm clothes to go outside? Describe what Peter experienced in the snow. What state of matter was the snow? What state of matter was the snow when it melted? Why did the snowball Peter put in his pocket disappear?

3. **Application:**
Imagine it snowed here tomorrow. Plan your activities for your snowy day. How would your environment change? Would you have to behave differently? Design a way for Peter to keep the snowball from melting. Plan what Peter would do on a "sunny day." How do people adapt to the weather? Give examples of how you adapt to the local weather throughout the year.

4. **Analysis:**
Identify ways the snow affected Peter and his surroundings. Why was the snow still on the ground the next day too? Compare and contrast a summer day to a snowy day.

5. **Synthesis:**
How does weather impact your daily life? Organisms? Environment? Predict what will happen to the snow when the sun does come out. Explain the process. What things are most important for keeping solid water frozen? Explain your thinking.

6. **Evaluation:**
Peter was happy when it snowed. Would you be happy if it snowed? Why or why not? Choose your favorite type of weather (sunny and warm, snowy and cold, rainy and cold, etc.). Why is this your favorite? Peter brought inside a snowball. Was this a good idea? Why or why not?

Follow-Up Activities

The Snowy Day

- Have students create a project that is a representation of a snowy day. Include things in the environment, activities that may occur inside or outside, plant and animal adaptations and words that are associated with winter.

- Go on a winter walk in and outside the school. Use all of their senses to make observations about the season of winter. Record observations and present to the class. Repeat throughout the year; create a book recording seasonal changes and observation walks.

- Rewrite *The Snowy Day* and illustrate the book for different types of weather. In groups, have students create their "day" by thinking of what they would do, wear, and see. Perform their stories for the community.

- Experiment with making snowballs using shaved ice. Make snowballs of various sizes and place in different areas throughout the class and outside to see the effects. Have students predict what will happen to the snowballs based on the size and location of the snowballs. Record and analyze their observations and determine the best characteristics and "living" conditions for the snowball.

- Research and investigate different states of matter. Explore with different materials and their abilities to change to a different state of matter. Relate the water cycle to the states of matter.

- Research other specific interests, curiosities, and basic information about seasons, winter, organisms, and states of matter. Provide and encourage the use of multiple sources of information. Have students share their learning in a variety of ways.

Someday a Tree

Written by: Eve Bunting
Published by: Clarion Books

Major Topics:

Environment – Issues, Changes
Organisms – Plants, Basic Needs, Behavior, Habitat, Life Cycle

National Science Education Content Standards (1996)

Life Science

- The Characteristics of Organisms
- Life Cycle of Organisms
- Organisms and Their Environments

Science in Personal and Social Perspectives

- Changes in the Environment

Summary:

Alice and her parents are dismayed when they realize that their favorite tree, which has been alive for generations and been a part of their lives for years, is dying. After consulting a tree doctor, they find out that the area surrounding the tree has been polluted. After many attempts by the family and community to save the tree, everyone realizes that this tree's life is slowly coming to an end. To help keep the tree "alive," Alice realizes she could plant some acorns which she had collected from the tree before it was sick. Now, someday, there will be another tree in its place, just as beautiful as the one they loved so much.

Science Concept Map

Someday a Tree

Eve Bunting

- Environmental issues, changes
  - Pollution
  - Conservation and preservation
  - Community building
- Organisms
  - Trees
    - Characteristics and responses
    - Environmental issues, changes
    - Relationships with people
    - Basic needs
    - Life cycle

Thinking Questions Based on Bloom's Taxonomy: *Someday a Tree*

1. **Knowledge:**
   What happened to the oak tree? What happened to the grass around the tree? List the different ways the community tried to save the tree. What did Alice do at the end of the book to help the tree? What did Alice collect from the tree?

2. **Comprehension:**
   How did Alice and her family figure out that the tree was sick? Why did the tree die? Explain why the tree was important to the family. Why did the community want to help save the tree? How did Alice "save" the tree? Why did the animals stop visiting the tree?

3. **Application:**
   Predict what would happen if someone dumped polluted water in the schoolyard. What would be affected? Imagine you have a small pond in your backyard. What would you do to save the living things in the pond if a harmful chemical was poured into it? If one of your special plants died, how could you replace it?

4. **Analysis:**
   Describe an oak tree's life cycle. How did the pollution affect the tree? Think about all of the interactions between humans and other animals and the tree. Categorize their effects on the tree as beneficial or harmful. Justify your decisions.

5. **Synthesis:**
   Imagine a community that is safe for all living things. What would it be like? What would be important? Discuss the relationship between humans and nature. Predict what will happen to the acorns that Alice planted.

6. **Evaluation:**
   Justify Alice's reasons for planting the acorns. Why is the relationship between humans and the environment so important? Alice's family and the community tried a lot of things to save the tree. Was this a good idea? Explain your opinion. Do you agree with the statement Alice's dad said that "no one can own a tree"? Explain your thinking.

Follow-Up Activities

Someday a Tree

- Experiment with growing two plants under different conditions. Have one plant grow in ideal conditions and the other with some type of pollution (soapy water, soil with oil, etc.). Compare and contrast the two plant's growth. Keep a record of observations. Determine the impact of the pollution.

- Research environmental issues (including pollution, conservation, and preservation). Design visuals to put around the school telling students how to keep their school and the Earth beautiful and healthy.

- Celebrate and emphasize Earth Day (April 22). Discuss and develop ways to give back to the Earth. Research the history of this day and current trends with environmental issues.

- Discuss a plant's life cycle and the role of seeds. Investigate seeds, their properties, types, and function. Compare and contrast different plants and how they reproduce. To share understanding, dramatize the life cycle of a tree or write and publish a class big book.

- Have students pretend they are "tree doctors," and write a prescription explaining how to keep all trees healthy. Contact local tree doctors, botanists, or the local arboretum to gather information. Create posters and other visuals to share the information.

- Adopt a tree around or near your school. Have students collect data (size, diameter, type, etc.) on the tree and observe it through the seasons. Develop a tree history and a guide that outlines how to best take care of the tree.

- Visit and investigate a local arboretum. Study the various trees, their physical properties, and the surrounding habitat. Keep field journals of their observations.

- Research other specific interests, curiosities, and basic information about organisms, plants, and environmental issues. Provide and encourage the use of multiple sources of information. Have students share their learning in a variety of ways.

Stellaluna

Written and Illustrated by: Janell Cannon
Published by: Harcourt Brace

Major Topics:

Organisms – Bats, Birds, Adaptations, Basic Needs, Behavior
Life Cycles, Physical Characteristics

National Science Education Content Standards (1996)

Life Science

- The Characteristics of Organisms
- Life Cycles of Organisms
- Organisms and Their Environments

Summary:
Stellaluna, a young fruit bat, gets separated from her mother in the forest when an owl attacks. She is taken in and raised by a bird mother who has three baby birds of her own. As Stellaluna spends more time with the bird family, she adopts many bird behaviors; she sleeps at night and eats insects. Once Stellaluna is reunited with her bat mother, she realizes that she naturally has bat behaviors and characteristics, unlike those of a bird. For example, she can see in the dark and hang upside down. After revisiting her bird family, Stellaluna and her bird friends realize that they are both similar and different in many ways. But most importantly, they are friends.

Science Concept Map

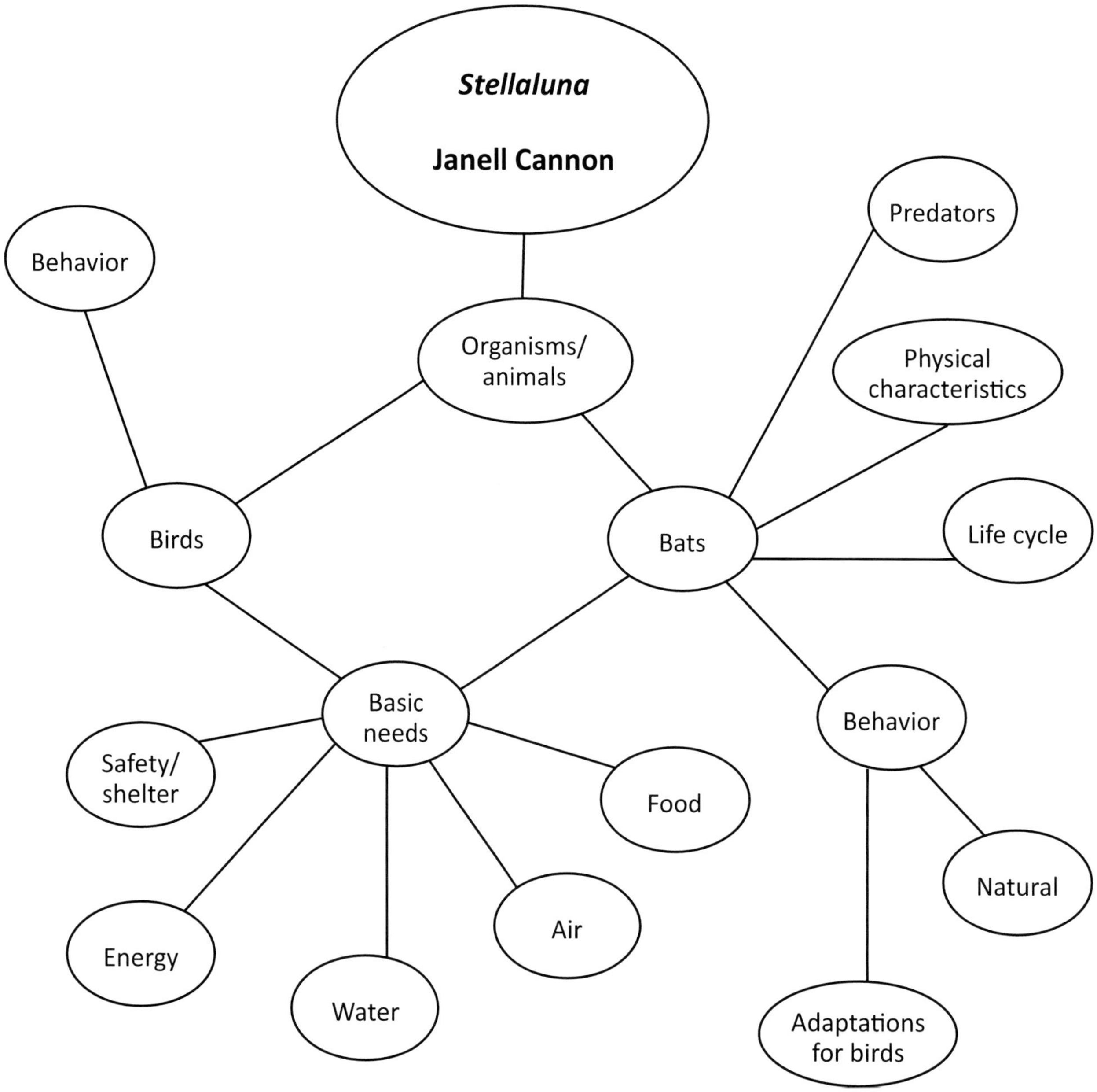

Stellaluna

Janell Cannon

Predators

Behavior

Organisms/ animals

Physical characteristics

Birds

Bats

Life cycle

Basic needs

Behavior

Safety/ shelter

Food

Natural

Air

Energy

Water

Adaptations for birds

Thinking Questions Based on Bloom's Taxonomy: *Stellaluna*

1. **Knowledge:**
   Name the different types of animals in this book. Who takes care of Stellaluna after she is separated from her mother? What things does Stellaluna learn how to do with the birds? Who helps Stellaluna realize her bat characteristics at the end of the book? What things does Stellaluna learn from her bat mother at the end?

2. **Comprehension:**
   How did Stellaluna get separated from her mother? How does Stellaluna stay alive without her bat mother? What are some unique characteristics of bats, as discussed in the story? Once Stellaluna is reunited with her bat mother, how does her life change?

3. **Application:**
   If the birds grew up with a bat family, what would they be like? Choose a different habitat for Stellaluna to fall into and decide how she would adapt to that life. Imagine that you, as a human, slept during the day and were awake at night (nocturnal). What characteristics would you need to adapt? What important life skills have you learned from the adults in your life?

4. **Analysis:**
   Compare and contrast birds and bats. Think about their physical characteristics and behaviors. Compare and contrast Stellaluna's life with the birds and her life with the bats. Determine which life was the most appropriate for Stellaluna.

5. **Synthesis:**
   What would Stellaluna's life be like if she had stayed with the birds forever? Imagine if you were raised by a different animal; how would you need to change? What things about you would not be able to change? How does an organism survive in a particular environment?

6. **Evaluation:**
   Did the mother bird do the right thing to raise Stellaluna as a bird? Justify your answer. Should Stellaluna have stayed with the bird family? Why or why not? Should Stellaluna have gone looking for her mother when she was first separated? Explain your thinking.

Follow-Up Activities

Stellaluna

- Study various types of bats. Examine characteristics of bats, such as being nocturnal and using echolocation. Also look at issues of how mother bats take care of their babies and why bats are important or helpful to habitats. Share findings in a variety of ways.

- Research predators of bats. Discuss the relationship between predators and prey. Compare and contrast other animals' predator and prey relationships. Rewrite *Stellaluna* without the owl character. Study the impact of this predator on the story and in real-life situations.

- Investigate other nocturnal animals. Develop a visual model and a written project about an animal. Generalize characteristics of these type of animals. Compare and contrast the characteristics of nocturnal and non-nocturnal (diurnal) animals. How does each type survive in its environment?

- Have students create a visual representation of a bird or bat in its natural habitat. Study and include information about basic needs, physical characteristics, behavior, and habitat.

- Have students write and perform a play/skit where the birds live as bats. Consider all aspects of this situation and incorporate the habitat and behavioral adaptations into the play/skit.

- Research other specific interests, curiosities, and basic information about birds, bats, and other organisms. Provide and encourage the use of multiple sources of information. Have students share their learning in a variety of ways.

The Sun Is My Favorite Star

Written and Illustrated by: Frank Asch
Published by: Gulliver Books/Harcourt

Major Topics:

Earth's Movement – Change, Shadows
Sun – Heat, Light

National Science Education Content Standards (1996)

Earth and Space Science

- Objects in the Sky
- Changes in the Earth and Sky

Physical Science

- Light, Heat, Electricity, and Magnetism

Summary:

A young child explains why, among all the stars in the galaxy, the Sun is her favorite. She describes how it wakes her in the morning, lights and heats the Earth, casts shadows across the ground, and even plays hide and seek with the clouds. Through her eyes, the reader is able to understand the importance of the Sun to the Earth and to the lives of all living things.

Science Concept Map

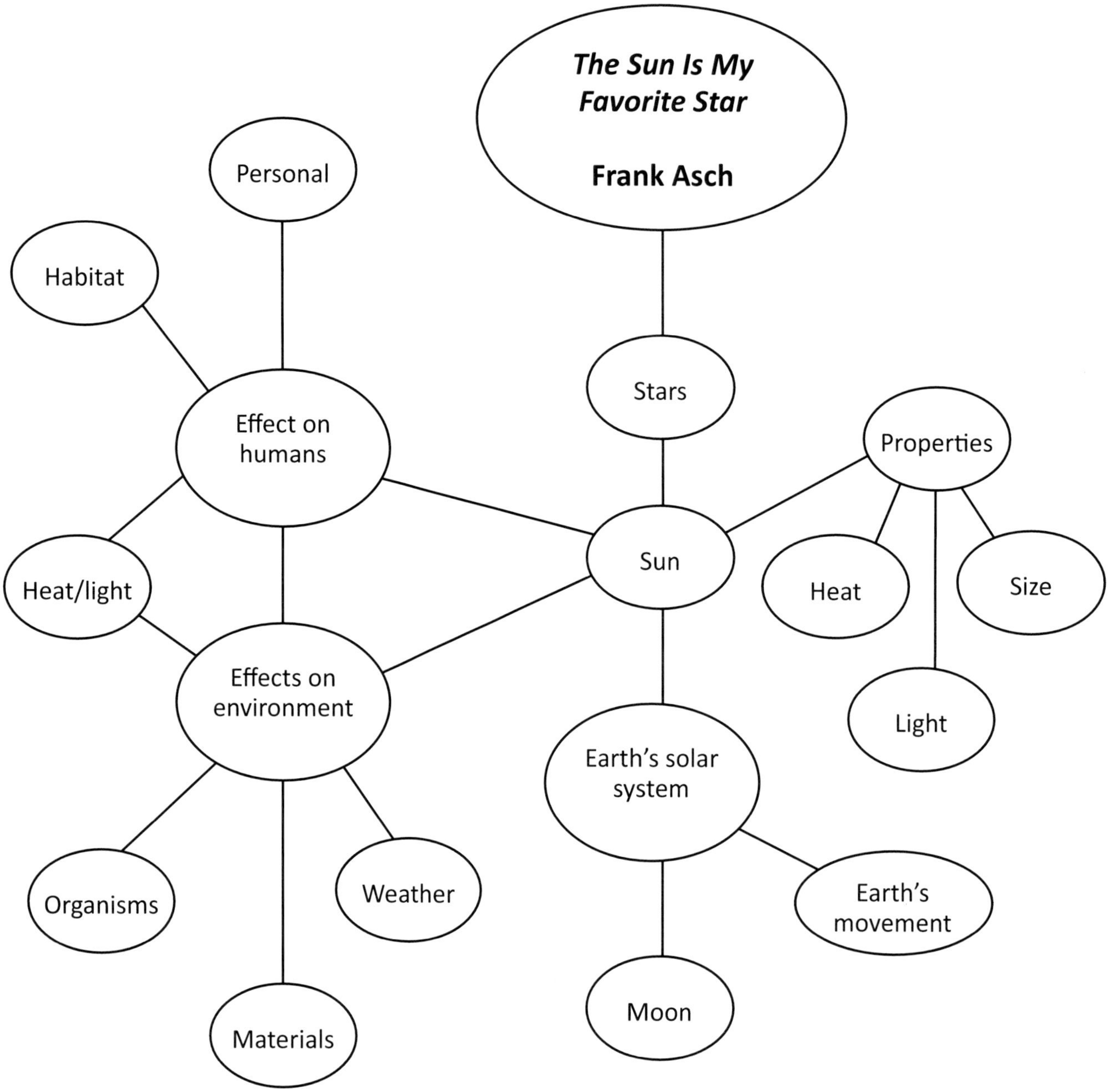

The Sun Is My Favorite Star

Frank Asch

Personal

Habitat

Stars

Effect on humans

Properties

Sun

Heat/light

Heat

Size

Effects on environment

Light

Earth's solar system

Organisms

Weather

Earth's movement

Moon

Materials

Thinking Questions Based on Bloom's Taxonomy: *The Sun Is My Favorite Star*

1. **Knowledge:**
   What is the Sun? Is the Sun the only star in the sky? What does the Sun do throughout the child's day?

2. **Comprehension:**
   Describe the Sun. What are some characteristics of the Sun? How does the Sun affect the child's day? How does the Sun play hide and seek with the child?

3. **Application:**
   Imagine there was no sunlight in your day. Predict what would happen to you and other things on Earth. In what ways does the Sun impact your day? Pretend tomorrow is going to be a warm and sunny day. Schedule your activities for the day. How else do you get light and heat?

4. **Analysis:**
   Imagine that the Sun was your only source of light or heat. How would your daily life be different? What activities could you only do during the day? Categorize the different ways the Sun affected the Earth and the child. Think about things involving heat, light, and movement. Why does the Sun appear to follow the child everywhere she goes?

5. **Synthesis:**
   Why is the Sun important to the Earth (people, plants, etc.)? Why is the Sun the child's favorite star?

6. **Evaluation:**
   Do you agree with the child that the Sun is the best star? Why or why not? Do you like the Sun? Explain your thinking. Do you prefer sunny or rainy days? Explain your thinking.

Follow-Up Activities

The Sun Is My Favorite Star

- Investigate the formation, properties, impacts and uses of the Sun for our lives. Have students survey friends and family. Interview scientists, energy specialists, and those that use the Sun in their jobs. Share findings in visual and written forms and/or create a play or skit that shows the life of the Sun.

- Research topics related to space and the solar system. Study stars and other objects in space and their functions. Look closely at the Earth's Sun and research basic facts as well as interesting discoveries, past and current.

- Conduct a class survey about students' favorite objects in the sky. Interview why students made the choices, analyze the data, and share their findings with the school. Publish a book entitled "Our Class Favorites."

- Demonstrate the heat of the Sun. Focus sunlight through a magnifying lens onto a bar of chocolate. Investigate why the chocolate heats and melts. Research light and heat, reflection, refraction, and absorption.

- Experiment with various materials to make a rainbow. Start with a dish of water, mirror, and sunlight. Based on the results, determine the critical components needed to make a rainbow.

- Explore the movement of the Sun across the sky. Have students go to a paved area with a partner and trace each other's shadows in the morning. Later in the day, have the students go back to the same spot, face their shadow again, and see what happened to their shadows. Discuss what happened and why.

- Research other specific interests, curiosities, and basic information about the Earth's movement, the Sun and other space-related topics. Provide and encourage the use of multiple sources of information. Have students share their learning in a variety of ways.

A Symphony of Whales

Written by: Steve Schuch
Published by: Voyager Books/Harcourt

Major Topics:

Environment – Interdependency
Organisms – Whales, Humans, Basic Needs, Behavior, Habitats
Technology

National Science Education Content Standards (1996)

Life Science

- The Characteristics of Organisms
- Organisms and Their Environments

Science in Personal and Social Perspectives

- Types of Resources
- Changes in the Environment
- Science and Technology in Local Challenges

Summary:

Glashka, an Eskimo girl, has the gift of being able to hear the songs of the ancient whale, Narna. When thousands of Beluga whales become trapped under the ice near her village, Glashka and the villagers make an all-call out over the radio for help. As they anxiously wait for an icebreaker, the villagers work together to save the whales, including chipping away the ice so the whales can have access to air and feeding them fish. The interdependence between the whales and the villagers becomes clear. When a Russian icebreaker arrives to help clear a pathway, the whales are resistant to follow it. Glashka's gift allows her to hear the whale's song and understand that they need to hear a certain type of music, human music, if they are to be led safely to the open sea. Even though the icebreaker clears the way, Glashka's ability to hear the whale's song is the crucial factor that saves the whales. This story is based on an actual event.

Science Concept Map

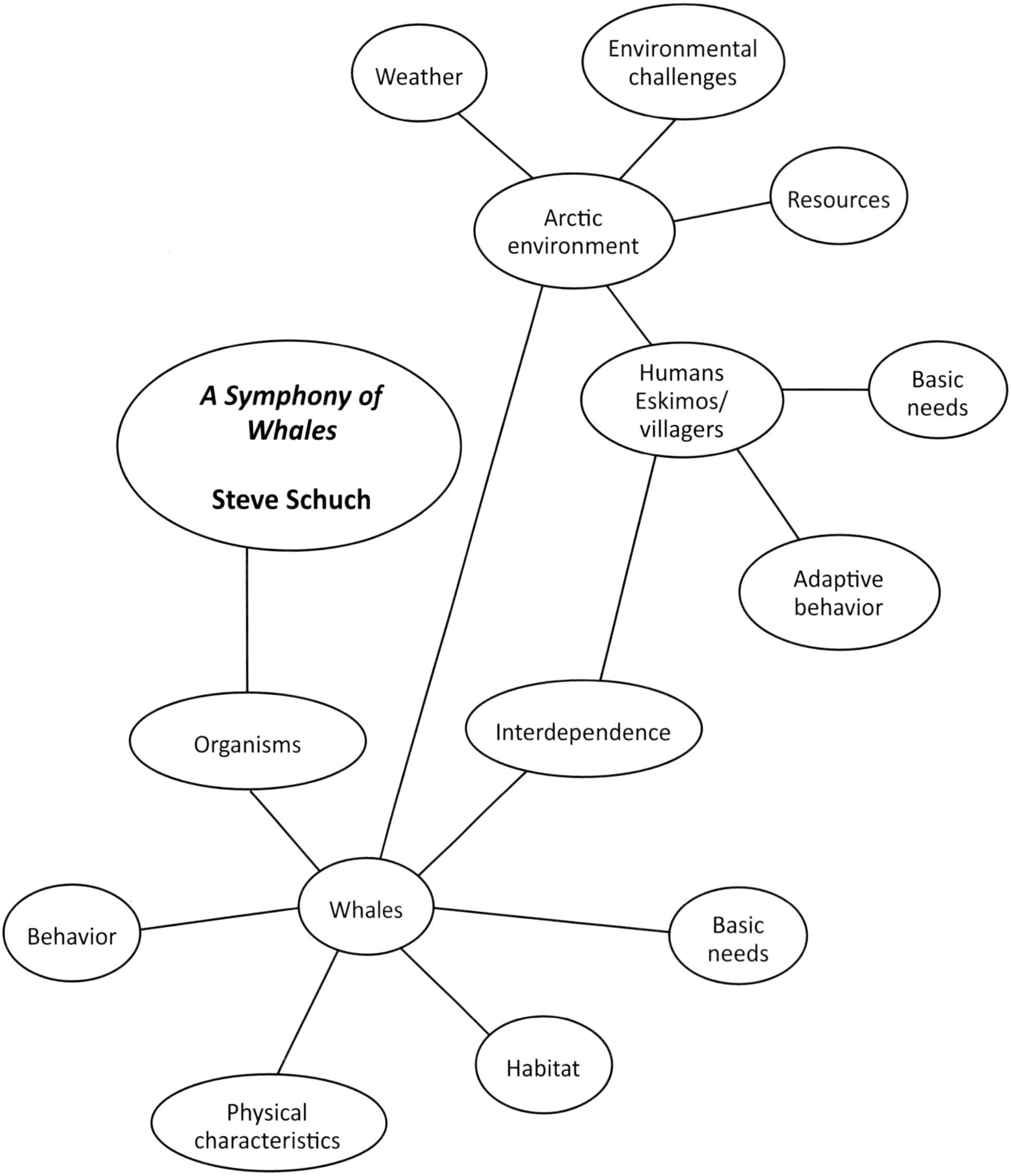

Thinking Questions Based on Bloom's Taxonomy:
A Symphony of Whales

1. **Knowledge:**
   What special gift did Glashka possess? What is the main problem in the story? Describe the weather. What did Glashka and her father do to save the whales? What did the villagers do to help the whales? Other than the villagers, what came to help the whales? Who found the whales first? What type of music helped to get the whales to freedom?

2. **Comprehension:**
   Why are the whales trapped in the ice? How did the older whales help the younger whales while they were trapped in the ice? How did the whales survive being trapped in the bay? Why do whales sing? Why could the icebreaker only stay for a short time? Why had the sea begun to freeze? How did the whales eventually leave the bay?

3. **Application:**
   If you found a trapped animal in your neighborhood, what could you do to save it? Think about how an animal could get trapped where you live. If the dogs had not heard the whales, predict what would have happened. How is your daily life dependent on the environment? Think of other times that teamwork has helped to save animals or people. Describe the examples.

4. **Analysis:**
   Compare and contrast whales and humans. How were the whales saved? Describe the process and outline the strategies used to help them survive. Categorize your thinking into groups by source of help (e.g., self-help, Eskimo, icebreaker). In what ways is the sea important to the survival of the people in Glashka's village?

5. **Synthesis:**
   All of the people in the village helped to sustain the whales. Why do you think everyone worked so hard together to save the whales? Explain the interdependence of the whales, sea, and the villagers.

6. **Evaluation:**
   By feeding the whales, the villagers depleted some of their limited food supply. Was this a good choice? Why or why not? At the end of the story the whales followed the icebreaker when classical music was played. What type of music would you follow? Explain your answer. If you were the captain of the icebreaker, would you have stayed and risked the lives of your own sailors to help the whales? Explain your opinion.

Follow-Up Activities

A Symphony of Whales

- Imagine that a whale is caught in waters in or near your state. Develop a plan to help sustain the life of that whale until it can be returned to safe waters with help from marine experts.

- Investigate different types of whales. Research interests and basic information. How are whales similar and different from other mammals? How is a whale similar and different from a fish? Study current environmental issues related to whales.

- When whales or other water animals are "beached" on American seashores, how are they taken care of? Who takes care of the animals? Find real-life examples. Contact aquariums, the coast guard, and other marine-life centers for information.

- Create a written or visual project that shows the interdependence in your own community among humans, animals, plants, and the environment.

- Explore with sound in water. Which types of sounds travel the best through water? How do whales hear sound? Investigate the different types of music from the story in water. Do they sound different? How do whales communicate? Create products to share their understanding.

- Have students rewrite the story from the whales' perspective. Take into consideration all of the aspects of the story. Dramatize the story for the school community.

- Research other specific interests, curiosities, and basic information about the arctic environment, whales, interdependency, environmental issues, and technology. Provide and encourage the use of multiple sources of information. Have students share their learning in a variety of ways.

The Tiny Seed

Written and Illustrated by: Eric Carle
Published by: Aladdin Paperbacks

Major Topics:

Organisms – Plants, Basic Needs, Behavior, Life Cycle, Physical Characteristics

National Science Education Content Standards (1996)

Life Science

- The Characteristics of Organisms
- The Life Cycle of Organisms
- Organisms and their Environments

Summary:

As the autumn wind arrives, many seeds, including the Tiny Seed, begin their life's journey by traveling through the air to distant places. The seeds experience many obstacles, including cold, icy weather, hungry birds, and scouring animals. The Tiny Seed, though, survives the harsh environments and continues its growth cycle by landing in a healthy environment. When winter passes and spring arrives, the Tiny Seed begins its new life and becomes a plant. The plant then meets even more obstacles, including other plants and children picking flowers. As time passes and the warmer months arrive, the Tiny Seed becomes a giant flower that is adored by many. As autumn arrives again, the giant flower begins to lose its petals. With the wind picking up, the flower's tiny seeds are carried off–and the life cycle continues.

Science Concept Map

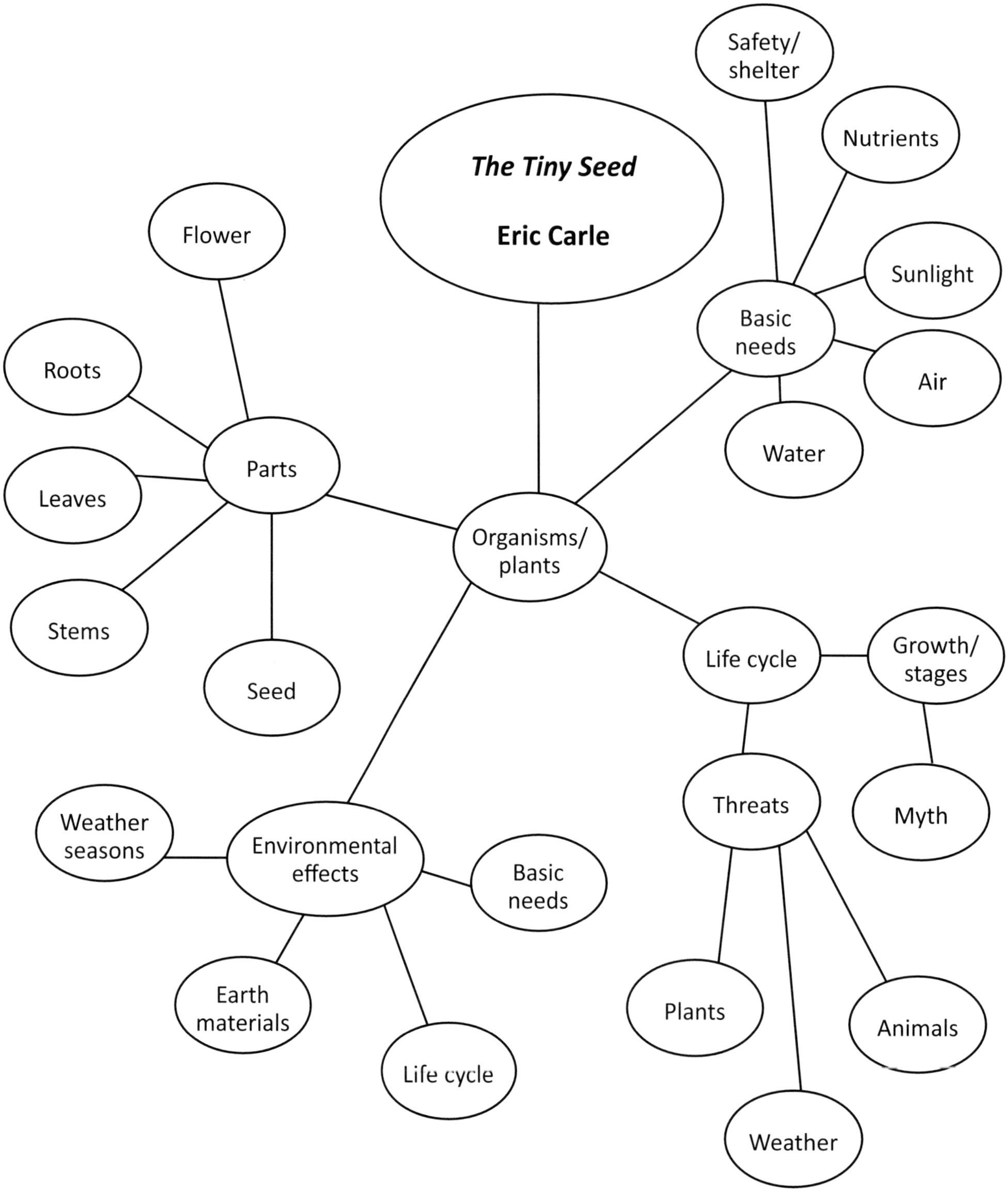

The Tiny Seed

Eric Carle

Organisms/ plants

Parts
Flower
Roots
Leaves
Stems
Seed

Basic needs
Safety/ shelter
Nutrients
Sunlight
Air
Water

Life cycle
Growth/ stages
Myth
Threats
Plants
Weather
Animals

Environmental effects
Weather seasons
Basic needs
Earth materials
Life cycle

Thinking Questions Based on Bloom's Taxonomy: *The Tiny Seed*

1. **Knowledge:**
   In what season did the Tiny Seed's life cycle begin? What caused the seeds to travel from land to land? What did the Tiny Seed eventually become? What happened to most of the other original seeds?

2. **Comprehension:**
   Retell the events of the story. Explain how the Tiny Seed grew into the giant flower. Why did the other seeds not survive? What types of challenges did the Tiny Seed have to get past to become a plant?

3. **Application:**
   Predict what would happen to flower seeds without sunlight, without water, and without soil. Think about your own life. What do you need to be able to grow? What challenges do you experience in your life? How do you get through them? Think about animals in the wild; what do they need to grow and survive? How about domestic animals?

4. **Analysis:**
   Categorize the different types of environmental factors that affected the life of the seed/plant. Compare and contrast the impact that each season had on the seeds. Why was each season important for this seed's life? Identify the basic needs of the Tiny Seed plant.

5. **Synthesis:**
   Predict what will happen to the seeds that get blown out of the flower's seedpod at the end of the story. Explain your ideas. Pretend someone gave you a tiny seed. How would you help the seed to survive and become a plant? Determine why the environment is important to the life of plants.

6. **Evaluation:**
   In which stage of the Tiny Seed's life cycle do you think it was most vulnerable? In which stage of a human's life cycle do you think he or she is most vulnerable? Justify your answers with reasons. In the story, children picked one of the flowers. Is this a good thing to do? Explain your thinking.

Follow-Up Activities

The Tiny Seed

- Research the life cycles of different plants. How are they the same? How do they differ? Compare and contrast the life cycles of different plants with other living organisms. Create a collection of life cycle visuals.

- Observe a plant over a long period of time. Identify its parts through the growth cycle. Maintain scientific journals to record observations and chart growth.

- Research and investigate the various ways seeds travel. Determine the benefit and purpose of each manner. Think about how a plant's environment and characteristics may impact the ways its seeds travel.

- How do seeds differ from one another? Collect different types of seeds. Consider how they are the same and different. Which seeds travel long distances with the wind, like the Tiny Seed? What adaptations do other seeds have that enable them to travel in other ways? Determine from what parts of plants different kinds of seeds come. Walk around your school yard and consider how the plants you see reproduce. Where are their seeds? Develop a "seed museum" where different types of seeds are showcased.

- Have students invent a plant that could survive in a particular environment that they imagine. Determine its physical characteristics, its growth cycle, and its responses, based on its environment. Choose a purposeful name for the new plant and create a visual representation with written background to share with others.

- Research other specific interests, curiosities, and basic information about plants and their environments. Provide and encourage the use of multiple sources of information. Have students share their learning in a variety of ways.

The Very Hungry Caterpillar

Written and Illustrated by: Eric Carle
Published by: The Putnam Publishing Group

Major Topics:

Organisms – Butterfly, Basic Needs, Behavior, Life Cycle

National Science Education Content Standards (1996)

Life Science

- The Characteristics of Organisms
- The Life Cycle of Organisms
- Organisms and Their Environments

Summary:

When a caterpillar hatches out of his egg, he is very hungry and eats everything he sees. For a week, he eats holes through different types of food, adding one more piece of food each day. After seven days of eating food that he just finds around, the caterpillar begins to get a stomachache. However, on the next Sunday, he eats a hole through a green leaf and feels much better. After deciding that he is not hungry any more, the caterpillar makes a cocoon in which to metamorphose. (Carle uses the word *cocoon*, which is scientifically incorrect: it should be *chrysalis*.) When the caterpillar emerges from the chrysalis, he is a beautiful adult butterfly.

Science Concept Map

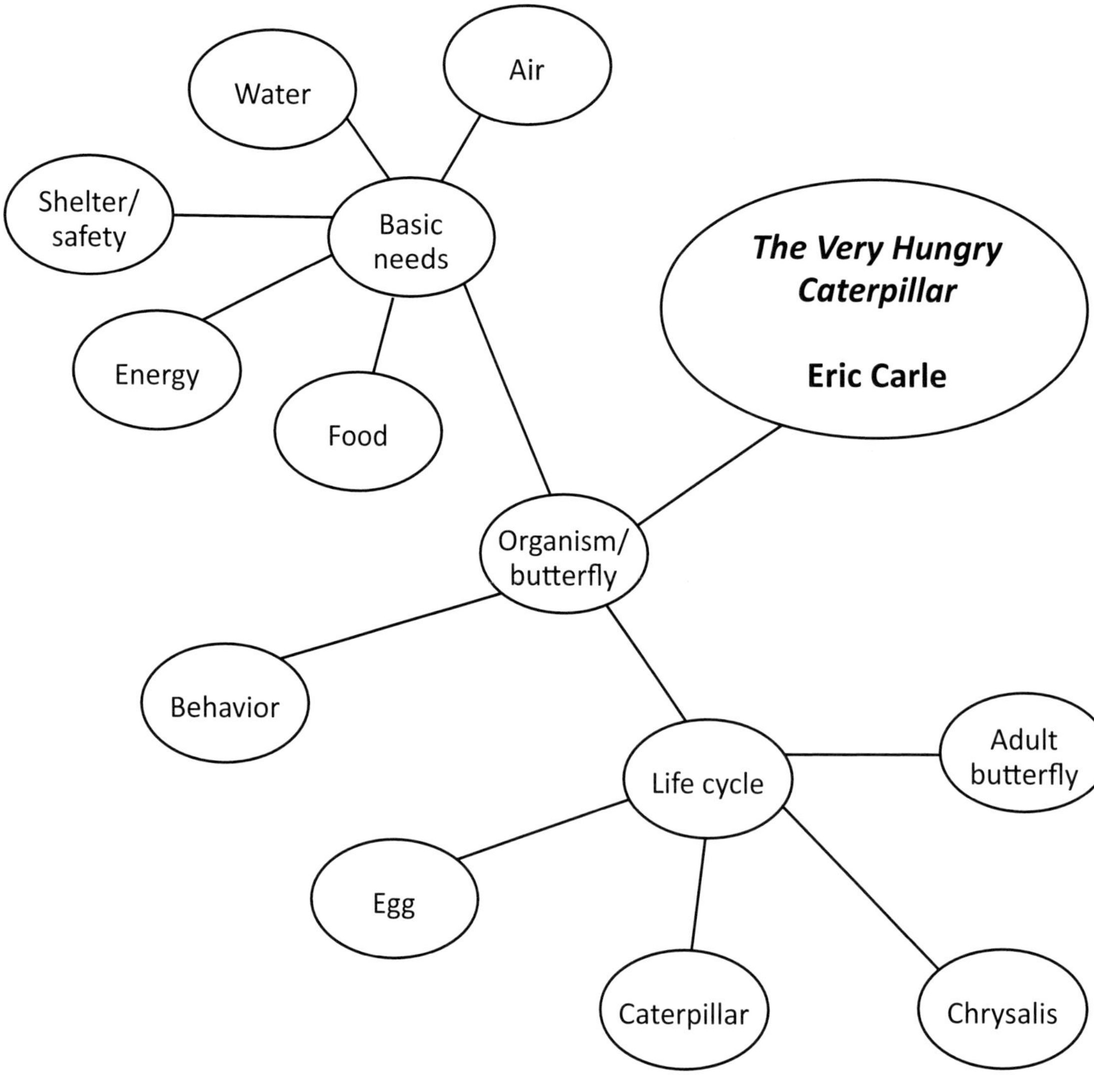

Thinking Questions Based on Bloom's Taxonomy: *The Very Hungry Caterpillar*

1. **Knowledge:**
   Where did the caterpillar come from? What did the caterpillar change into as an adult? List things that the caterpillar ate while he was hungry. What did he eat that finally filled him up and did not make him sick?

2. **Comprehension:**
   Describe each stage of the butterfly's life. How did the caterpillar change into a butterfly? What things does a butterfly need to survive and grow? What foods do you think gave the caterpillar a stomachache? Why did the caterpillar feel better after eating the leaf?

3. **Application:**
   Name other animals that go through a metamorphosis; compare and contrast with a butterfly. What food items make you sick if you eat a lot of them? Which ones are healthier for you? What things do you need, as a human, to survive and grow?

4. **Analysis:**
   Categorize the life stages of a butterfly. In which season was the caterpillar born? How is the chrysalis important to the life cycle of a butterfly? Why did the caterpillar need to eat so much food? Compare and contrast the stages.

5. **Synthesis:**
   Are all caterpillars "very hungry"? Why or why not? What would have happened if the caterpillar had no food? Explain the relationship between the caterpillar and the butterfly. Imagine you are creating a butterfly habitat; think of what would be needed to support the butterfly's growth and survival.

6. **Evaluation:**
   Which life stage of the butterfly do you think is the most important? The most fragile? Defend your answer. Should the butterfly have eaten the candy? How about the fruit? Explain your opinion.

Follow-Up Activities

The Very Hungry Caterpillar

- As a class, design and set up a butterfly garden. Research and investigate the necessary components to best create a butterfly habitat. Observe as eggs hatch, caterpillars make chrysalides, and butterflies emerge. Record how many days each stage lasts depending on the species. Compare and contrast the life cycles of different butterflies.

- Investigate butterflies native to your local area. Use readily available information as well as collect data by exploring. Create a field guide with visuals and characteristics of each butterfly.

- Compare and contrast the life cycle of a butterfly to the life cycle of a moth. Have students illustrate and discuss the different life stages and other differences in physical characteristics.

- Have students pretend they are butterflies. Through movement, model the four stages of their life cycle. Add complexity by creating a performance of a butterfly's life cycle in certain environments with added narration.

- Research other animals that go through a metamorphosis, such as mealworms and frogs. Compare and contrast the life cycles of those animals with the butterfly.

- Research other specific interests, curiosities, and basic information about butterflies, metamorphosis and other organisms. Provide and encourage the use of multiple sources of information. Have students share their learning in a variety of ways.

What Will the Weather Be Like Today?

Written by: Paul Rogers
Published by: Scholastic, Inc.

Major Topics:

Organisms – Animals/Humans, Plants, Basic Needs, Behavior, Habitat
Weather – Types, Environment Changes

National Science Education Content Standards (1996)

Life Science

- The Characteristics of Organisms
- Organisms and Their Environments

Earth and Space Science

- Properties of Earth Materials
- Objects in the Sky
- Changes in the Earth and Sky

Summary:

"What will the weather be like today?" is the question addressed in many ways in this book. The book is based on different types of weather in various locations and how it affects different environments and meets the needs of organisms. For example, on a warm day, people and other animals are swimming and playing outdoors; the lizard prefers to live where the weather is dry. Different places around the world are shown with different types of weather, from dry deserts to snowy mountains. Different organisms express their weather preferences. In each type of weather, the behavior of people, plants, and animals can be seen and the characteristics of the land explored. The book ends by asking the reader, "How is the weather where you are today?"

Science Concept Map

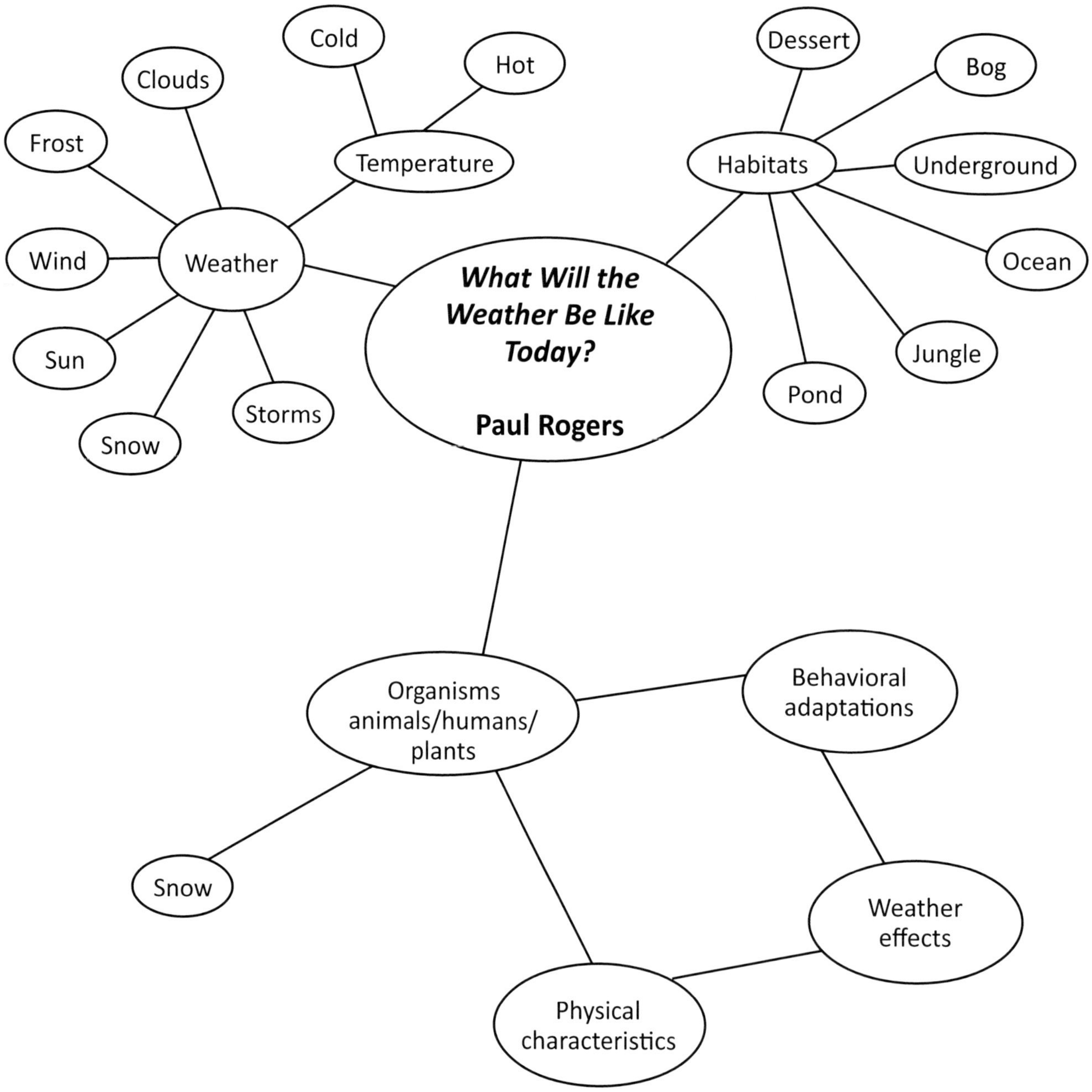

Thinking Questions Based on Bloom's Taxonomy: *What Will the Weather Be Like Today?*

1. **Knowledge:**
What types of weather are shared in the book? What two types of weather are needed to make a rainbow? What do people usually do when it's rainy? Sunny? Snowy? What type of weather does the duck prefer? The frog? The lizard?

2. **Comprehension:**
What things are affected by the weather? Why would a frog want it to rain? Why would a lizard prefer dry weather and not want it to rain? Why do people react to the weather?

3. **Application:**
Discuss other ways animals and humans adapt to the weather. How would you adapt to a desert or a jungle? What would you wear? What would you do? Describe what happens on a windy day, a stormy day, and a cloudy day in your town. What type of weather do you think a giraffe would like? Why? Discuss ways that sudden changes in weather affect the environment, people, and animals. What would happen if an environment's weather changed drastically? For example, if the desert suddenly got a lot of rain or there was a hurricane.

4. **Analysis:**
Compare and contrast the typical weather in deserts, in jungles, on snowy mountains, and in your town. What effects do wind, storms, hot weather, and cold weather have on people? Generate a list of behaviors that people and other animals do when it is snowy, sunny, windy, and stormy. Think of animals that live in different places. Classify the animals by the type of climate they need. Discuss why.

5. **Synthesis:**
Assume you are one of the animals in the story and explain why you prefer a certain type of weather and how that type of weather impacts your behavior. Pretend you are a human living in one of the different locations in the book. Explain why you are behaving in those ways.

6. **Evaluation:**
Which type of weather do you prefer? Justify your answer to the class. If you could pick a new environment to live, where would you live? Why?

Follow-Up Activities

What Will the Weather Be Like Today?

- Have students create an imaginary animal and determine its appropriate habitat. Determine what this animal needs, based on its physical characteristics and behaviors, to survive. Consider which environment would best meet its needs. Develop a class animal museum.

- Invite a meteorologist to share his or her expertise and answer questions about how he or she predicts the weather. Ask questions about weather prediction, patterns, and curiosities.

- Observe the weather during each of the seasons. Chart the temperature, observe changes in landforms, plants, and animals, and notice human activities. Develop a weather observation journal. Include in the journal all things that are affected by the weather. Analyze weather patterns and trends.

- Research an animal that lived during the Ice Age. Report on how the weather affected the animal and how it would have to change to live in our present times.

- Compare and contrast animals of the same species that live in different environments (e.g., polar bear, brown bear, and/or a panda). Study the differences in their physical characteristics and behavior.

- Have students survey friends and family. Research what things people need and like to do in different types of weather. Synthesize the data and share with the community.

- Research other specific interests, curiosities, and basic information about organisms and weather. Provide and encourage the use of multiple sources of information. Have students share their learning in a variety of ways.

When Winter Comes

Written by: Nancy Van Laan
Published by: Simon & Schuster

Major Topics:

Earth's Movements – Seasons, Winter, Changes
Organisms – Animals/Humans, Plants, Basic Needs, Behavior, Habitat
Weather – Patterns, Effects

National Science Education Content Standards (1996)

Life Science

- The Characteristics of Organisms
- Organisms and Their Environments

Earth and Space Science

- Changes in the Earth and Sky

Summary:

Earth's environment goes through many seasonal changes. This story explores the question, "What happens when winter comes?" As it grows colder, the trees and plants begin to change; the animals naturally seek warmer habitats or adapt to the environment; and humans behave in certain ways — when winter comes.

Science Concept Map

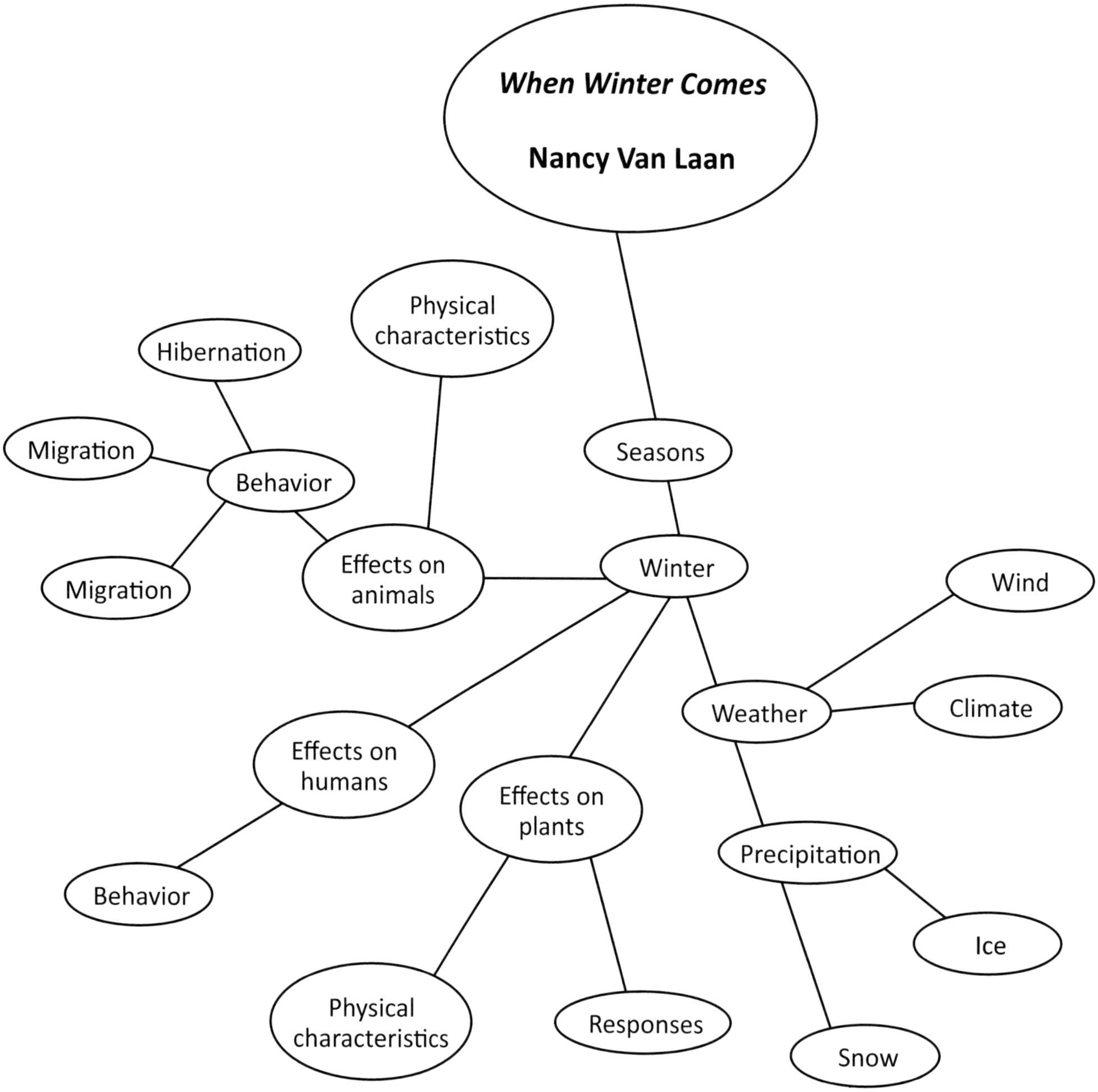

Thinking Questions Based on Bloom's Taxonomy: *When Winter Comes*

1. **Knowledge:**
   What happens when winter comes in the story? Name different things that change when winter comes.

2. **Comprehension:**
   Describe the winter environment in the story. Based on the story, what types of weather are typical in the winter? How do the animals in the story adapt to the winter? How do the trees change?

3. **Application:**
   What adaptations do you make in order to live in the winter? Summer? Spring? Fall? How do plants and animals in your local area adapt to each season? If a plant or animal cannot adapt to an environmental change, what happens? Why?

4. **Analysis:**
   Classify the changes in the environment when winter comes. Think about specific changes in the weather, plants, animals, and people. Compare and contrast the effects of winter on humans and other animals, and on animals versus plants.

5. **Synthesis:**
   Describe the common types of weather for each season in your local area. Answer and discuss the question from the beginning of the story, "Where do the leaves go in the winter?" How do the plants, animals, and humans adapt to seasonal changes?

6. **Evaluation:**
   Pretend you live in a place that experienced only one season or type of weather all year long. What season would you want it to be? Explain your choice. In winter, would you rather be an animal that burrows like the field mouse, or migrates such as the songbird? Explain your thinking.

Follow-Up Activities

When Winter Comes

- Brainstorm a list of animals. Determine which animals hibernate, migrate, or change in other ways in the winter. Dramatize how the animals behave in winter.

- Compare and contrast a typical environment/habitat in winter to the same environment/habitat in summer. Think about the weather and the various adaptations and behaviors of plants, animals, and humans. How would the animals, trees, and plants look different during the summer than they would during the winter? Create a class book called *When Summer Comes*. Create similar books for each of the other seasons as well.

- Read the book *The Same Day in March* by Marilyn Singer. Analyze the weather differences in the month of March throughout the world. Then select a typical winter day. Create scenes of how this day would appear based on different locations throughout the world. Develop a project, "The Same Day in January."

- Have students construct their own winter survival kit for outdoors based on their local area. Have students consider their own basic needs, like nutrients, water, energy, and shelter/safety.

- Research various plants. Determine how different plants react to weather patterns throughout the seasons. Study groups of plants like annuals, perennials, bulbs, deciduous trees, and evergreen trees. Develop scientific field guides based on the research.

- Look at seasonal changes around the country. Compare and contrast seasons in different states or regions. Be sure to include Hawaii and Alaska. Relate the seasonal change with the Earth's movement around the Sun.

- Learn from schools around the world. Write letters or e-mails to schools in different locations and study their seasons. During each season, share pictures and descriptions describing the weather. Develop a project, "Weather Around the World."

- Research other specific interests, curiosities, and basic information about organisms, weather, and seasons. Provide and encourage the use of multiple sources of information. Have students share their learning in a variety of ways.

U-STARS~PLUS

Science & Literature Connections

Appendices

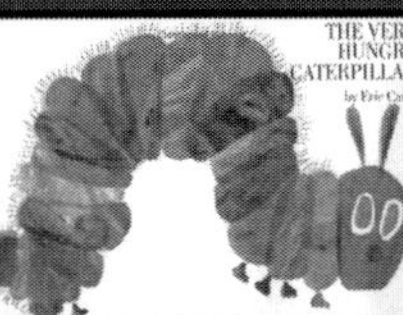

Appendix A
Book List
Science & Literature Connections

Aardema, V. (1981). *Bringing the rain to Kapiti Plain*. New York, NY: Penguin Group.

Asch, F. (1985). *Moonbear's shadow*. New York, NY: Aladdin Paperbacks.

Asch, F. (2000). *The sun is my favorite star*. New York, NY: Gulliver Books/Harcourt.

Baker, K. (1989). *The magic fan*. New York, NY: Voyager Books/Harcourt.

Barrett, J. (1978). *Cloudy with a chance of meatballs*. New York, NY: Aladdin Paperbacks.

Bruchac, J. (1993). *The first strawberries*. New York, NY: Dial Books for Young Readers.

Bunting, E. (1993). *Someday a tree*. New York, NY: Clarion Books.

Cannon, J. (1993). *Stellaluna*. New York, NY: Harcourt Brace.

Carle, E. (1987). *The tiny seed*. New York, NY: Aladdin Paperbacks.

Carle, E. (1987). *The very hungry caterpillar*. New York, NY: The Putnam Publishing Group.

Cherry, L. (1990). *The great Kapok tree: A Tale of the Amazon Rain Forest*. New York, NY: Voyager Books/Harcourt.

Cole, H. (1998). *I took a walk*. New York, NY: Greenwillow Books.

Collins, R. (2004). *Germs*. New York, NY: Bloomsbury Children's Books.

Dewey, J. O. (2002). *Once I knew a spider*. New York, NY: Walker.

Ehlert, L. (1995). *Snowballs*. New York, NY: Scholastic.

References

Fife, D. H. (1991). *The empty lot*. San Francisco, CA: Sierra Club Books for Children.

Heller, R. (1983). *The reason for a flower*. New York, NY: Penguin Putnam Books for Young Readers.

Hesse, K. (1999). *Come on, rain!* New York, NY: Scholastic.

Keats, E. J. (1962). *The snowy day*. New York, NY: Scholastic.

Lionni, L. (1969). *Alexander and the wind-up mouse*. New York, NY: Dragonfly Books.

Lionni, L. (1970). *Fish is fish*. New York, NY: Dragonfly Books.

Locker, T. (with Christiansen, C.; 1995). *Sky tree*. New York, NY: HarperCollins.

Luenn, N. (1992). *Mother earth*. New York, NY: Aladdin Paperbacks.

McCloskey, R. (1941). *Make way for ducklings*. New York, NY: The Viking Press.

Pfister, M. (1997). *Milo and the magical stones*. New York, NY: North-South Books.

Rogers, P. (1989). *What will the weather be like today?* New York, NY: Scholastic.

Schuch, S. (1999). *A symphony of whales*. New York, NY: Voyager Books/Harcourt.

Seuss, Dr. (1971). *The Lorax*. New York, NY: Random House.

Sharmat, M. (1980). *Gregory, the terrible eater*. New York, NY: Scholastic.

Showers, P. (1961). *The listening walk*. New York, NY: HarperCollins.

Van Laan, N. (2000). *When winter comes*. New York, NY: Simon & Schuster.

Appendix B

Content Index

Science & Literature Connections

Book Title	Page Numbers	Earth	Earth's Movement/ Seasons	Environment	Living and Non-Living Things	Organisms	Personal Health	Resources	Sound	States of Matter	Sun	Technology	Seather
Alexander and the Wind-Up Mouse	33												
Bringing the Rain to Kapiti Plain	37												
Cloudy With a Chance of Meatballs	41												
Come On, Rain!	47												
The Empty Lot	51												
The First Strawberries	57												
Fish is Fish	61												
Germs	65												
The Great Kapok Tree	69												
Gregory, the Terrible Eater	73												
I Took a Walk	77												
The Listening Walk	81												
The Lorax	85												
The Magic Fan	91												
Make Way for Ducklings	95												
Milo and the Magical Stones	99												

Appendix B

Content Index

Science & Literature Connections

(continued)

Book Title	Page Numbers	Earth	Earth's Movement/ Seasons	Environment	Living and Non-Living Things	Organisms	Personal Health	Resources	Sound	States of Matter	Sun	Technology	Seather
Moonbear's Shadow	103		■										
Mother Earth	107	■		■				■					
Once I Knew a Spider	111					■							
The Reason for a Flower	115					■		■					
Rocks in My Pockets	119	■				■		■					■
The Sky Tree	123		■			■							■
Snowballs	127							■		■			■
The Snowy Day	131		■			■				■			■
Someday a Tree	135			■		■							
Stellaluna	139					■							
The Sun Is My Favorite Star	143		■								■		
A Symphony of Whales	147			■		■						■	
The Tiny Seed	151					■							
The Very Hungry Caterpillar	155					■							
What Will the Weather Be Like Today?	159					■							■
When Winter Comes	163		■			■							■

Appendix C
Evidence Base for *U-STARS~PLUS*

The term *evidence-based* is currently being used in a variety of ways. It is generally used to show that a body of work has reached a threshold of reliability and/or validity. Evidence-based practice is not synonymous with research-based practice. Three things are essential in establishing the evidence base for a practice: the research base, the wisdom of respected practitioners, and the values held by the community that will be implementing the practice.

The *research base* for a practice is built over years of looking at how the practice works in a variety of settings, under a variety of circumstances, and with a variety of constituents. This research base takes time to build and, for the most part, is reflected in publications that are peer-reviewed where colleagues adjudicate the work (i.e., research journals). A research base is also tied to a theoretical base which anchors the practice within a larger body of research. Thus, the theories are both developed from and continue to inform the evidence base for a practice.

The *wisdom of practitioners*, which is equally important in the establishment of a practice as evidence-based, is generally seen through the wide adoption of the practice, the acceptance of the practice by key advocates and organizations, the transmission of the practice through standards and guidelines that are accepted by the field, and through publications that are practitioner oriented (e.g., teacher journals). At this point the practice also influences policies.

Finally, to be useful, the practice must fit well with the *values* of those who will be using it. The evidence base must respond to the core ideas and beliefs held by those who implement the practice because they feel that it addresses their needs. This response is seen through the commitment made to implement the practice and through the inclusion of the practice at all levels of implementation. Generally this commitment is fostered by the success seen during the early implementation of a practice and, as a result, support for the practice grows — rather than diminishes.

In sharing the evidence base for *U-STARS~PLUS*, we have included the research base through peer-reviewed articles and the practitioners' wisdom through teacher journals for each of our five core beliefs. This evidence base is also reflected in the acceptance of this work across five states and its current implementation in over 50 school districts. Our partnerships with the Council for Exceptional Children, the Morehead Planetarium and Science Center, and the North Carolina Association for Gifted and Talented further strengthen the evidence base.

U-STARS~PLUS Core Beliefs

Hands-on/inquiry science promotes thinking, achievement, and language development in young children and is especially useful in working with children from culturally/linguistically diverse and/or economically disadvantaged families.

AIMS Education Foundation. (2001). *AIMS-- Activities Integrating Mathematics and Science.* Fresno, CA: Author.

Ajello, T. (2000). Science journals: Writing, drawing, and learning. *Teaching K–8, 30*(5), 56–57.

Akerson, V., Flick, L., & Lederman, N. (2000). The influence of primary children's ideas in science on teaching practice. *Journal of Research in Science Teaching, 37*, 363–385.

Allen-Sommerville, L.(1996) Capitalizing on diversity: Strategies for customizing your curriculum to meet the needs of all students. *Science Teacher, 63*(2), 20–23.

Allington, R. L. (2002, June). What I've learned about effective reading instruction: From a decade of studying exemplary elementary classroom teachers. *Phi Delta Kappan, 83*, 740.

Amaral, O. M., Garrison, L., & Klentschy, M. (2002). Helping English learners increase achievement through inquiry-based science instruction. *Bilingual Research Journal, 26*(2), 214–239.

Basile, C. G. (1999, September). Collecting data outdoors: Making connections to the real world. *Teaching Children Mathematics, 6*(1), 8–11.

Behm, C. (2001). Big picture science. Uncovering teaching strategies for underrepresented groups. *Science Teacher, 68*(3), 37–39.

Bennett, A. T., & Kessler, J. H. (1996). *Apples, bubbles, and crystals: Your science ABCs.* New York, NY: Learning Triangle Press.

Bennett, A. T., & Kessler, J. H. (1998). *Sunlight, skyscrapers, and soda pop: The wherever-you-look science book.* Washington, DC: American Chemical Society.

Bergland, K., & Pakaluk, D. (2000). Writing: A vibrant part of science. *Teaching K–8, 30*(3), 47–49.

Bernhardt, E., Hirsch, G., Teemant, A., & Rodriguez-Munoz, M. (1996). Language diversity & science: Science for limited English proficiency students. *Science Teacher, 63*(2), 24–27.

Bjork, J. (2005). Teaching through trade books: From sap to syrup. *Science & Children, 43*(3), 16–18.

Boothe, D., & Stanley, J. C. (Eds.). (2004). *In the eyes of the beholder: Critical issues for diversity in gifted education*. Waco, TX: Prufrock Press.

Carlson, C. (2000). Scientific literacy for all: Helping English language learners make sense of academic language. *Science Teacher, 64*(3), 48–52.

Carnegie-IAS. (2009). *The opportunity equation: Transforming mathematics and science education for citizenship and the global economy.* Retrieved from http://www.opportunityequation.org/report/urgency-opportunity/

Center for Science, Mathematics, and Engineering Education. (2000). *Educating teachers of science, mathematics, and technology: New practices for the new millennium.* Washington, DC: National Academy Press.

Cheong, W. (2000, March/April). The power of questioning. *Connect*, 9–10.

Cherry, L. (2006). Trade books for learning: An author's view. *Science & Children, 44*(3), 44–47.

Ciborowski, J. (1992). *Textbooks and the students who can't read them: A guide to teaching content*. Boston, MA: Brookline Books.

Colangelo, N., Assouline, S. G., & Gross, M. U. M. (2004). A Nation deceived: How schools hold back America's brightest students. In *Templeton National Report on Acceleration. Volume 1.* Iowa City, IA: University of Iowa.

Colburn, A., & Echevarria, J. (1999). *Meaningful lessons. Science learning for all celebrating cultural diversity.* Retrieved from http://www.nsta.org/store/product_detail.aspx?id=10.2505/9780873551946

Coltrane, S. S., & Coleman, M. R. (2005, Fall/Winter). Using science as a vehicle: Search for outstanding potential in underserved populations. *Gifted Education Communicator*, 20–23.

Coskie, T. L. (2006). The synergy of science and reading. *Science & Children, 44*(3), 62–63.

Darity, W., Castellino, D., & Tyson, K. (2001). *Report on increasing opportunity to learn via access to rigorous courses and programs: One strategy for closing the achievement gap for at-risk and ethnic minority students* (Report No. ED459303). Raleigh, NC: North Carolina Department of Public Instruction.

Donnellan, K., & Roberts, G. (1985). What research says: Activity-based elementary science: A double bonus. *Science and Children, 22*(4), 119–121.

El-Hindi, A. (2003). Teaching ideas: Integrating literacy and science in the classroom. *Reading Teacher, 56*, 536–538.

Farland, D. (2006). Trade books and the human endeavor of science. *Science & Children, 44*(3), 35–37.

Ford, D., Baytops, J., & Harmon, D. (1997). Helping gifted minority students reach their potential: Recommendations for change. *Peabody Journal of Education, 72*(3/4), 201–216.

Ford, D. J. (2004). Scaffolding preservice teachers' evaluation of children's science literature. Attention to science-focused genres and use. *Journal of* Science *Teacher Education, 15*, 133–153.

Glenn Commission. (2000). *Before it's too late.* The National Commission on Mathematics and Science Teaching. Retrieved from http:www2.ed.gov/inits/Math/glenn/index.html

Gomez-Zwiep, S., & Straits. W. (2006). Analyzing anthromorphisms. *Science & Children, 44*(3), 26–29.

Hambrick, A., & Svedkauskaite, A. (2005). *Remembering the child: On equity and inclusion in mathematics and science classrooms.* Retrieved from www.ncrel.org/sdrs/areas/issues/content/cntareas/math/ma800.htm

Hapgood, S., & Palincsar, A. S. (2006–2007). Where literacy and science intersect. *Educational Leadership, 64*(4), 56–60.

Haury, D. (1993). *Teaching science through inquiry*. Columbus, OH: ERIC Clearinghouse for Science, Mathematics, and Environmental Education. (ERIC Digest No. 359 048).

Humphreys, J. (2000). Exploring nature with children. *Young Children,* 55(2), 16–20.

Jackson, J., Allen, G., & Dickinson, G. (2008). Connections charts and book talk groups. *Science & Children*, *46*(3), 27–31.

Kuldell, N. (2003). Read like a scientist to write like a scientist: Using authentic literature in the classroom. *Journal of College Science Teaching, 33*(2), 32–35.

Ladd, G. T. (1994). Science? Poetry? Let's have a contest. *Teaching K–8*, *24*(5), 46–50.

Lawrence Hall of Science, University of California. (2003). *GEMS: Great explorations in math and science.* Berkeley, CA: Author.

Lloyd, C., & Contreras, N. (1987). What research says: Science inside and out. *Science & Children, 25*, 30–31.

Lovedahl, A. N., & Bricker, P. (2006). Using biographies in science class. *Science & Children, 44*(3), 38–43.

Mesa, J. C., Klosterman, M. L., & Cronin-Jones, L. L., (2008). The poetry of science: A flexible tool for assessing elementary student science journals. *Science & Children*, *46*(3), 36–41.

Monhardt, L., & Monhardt, R. (2006). Creating a context for the learning of science process skills through picture books. *Early Childhood Education Journal, 34*, 66–71.

Mott, B. (2000). Observation as a springboard. *Connect*, *13*(5), 11–13.

Mrazek, R. (1994). *Teaching science in the 1990s*. Canada: The University of Lethbridge. Retrieved from http://fusion.uleth.ca/crdc/rick/rickcvsite/pdfs/teachsci90s.pdf

Murray, J., & Bartelmay, K. (2005). Inventors in the making. *Science & Children*, *42*(4), 40–44.

National Academy of Sciences. (2007). *Executive summary. Taking science to school: Learning and teaching science in grades K–8.* Retrieved from http://www.nap.edu/catalog.php?record_id=11625

National Research Council. (1996). *National Science Educational Standards*. Washington, DC: National Academy Press.

National Science Education Standards. (1996). *Science Content Standards: K–4, Chapter 6.* Retrieved from http://www.nap.edu/openbook.php?record_id=4962&page=103.

National Science Foundation. (2006). *America's pressing challenge—building a stronger foundation.* National Science Board. Retrieved from http://www.nsf.gov/statistics/nsb0602/

National Science Teachers Association. (2004). *Position statement. Scientific inquiry.* Arlington, VA: Author

National Science Teachers Association. (2007). *Position statement. Principles of professionalism for science educators.* Arlington, VA: Author.

Nelson, G., & Landel, C. (2006–2007). A collaborative approach for elementary science. *Educational Leadership, 64*(4), 72–75.

Nyberg, L., & McCloskey, S. (2008). Integration with integrity. *Science & Children, 46*(3), 46–49.

Pell, T., & Jarvis, T. (2001). Developing attitude to science scales for use with children of ages from five to eleven years. *International Journal of Science Education, 23,* 847–862.

Pratt, H. (2005). Where are we now? *Science & Children, 42*(4), 14–15.

Quinones, C., & Jeanpierre, B. (2005). Planting the spirit of inquiry. *Science & Children, 42*(7), 33–35.

Raines, S., & Canady, R. (1991). *More story stretchers: More activities to expand children's favorite books.* Mt. Ranier, MD: Gryphon House.

Rappe Zales, C., & Unger, C. S. (2008). The science and literacy framework. *Science & Children, 46*(3), 42–45.

Redmond, M. L. (2000). Storytelling and science. *Teaching K–8, 30*(7), 48–49.

Resnick, L. B, & Resnick, D. P. (1992). Assessing the thinking curriculum: New tools for educational reform. In B. R. Gifford, & M. C. O'Connor (Eds.), *Changing assessments: Alternative views of aptitude, achievement and instruction* (pp. 37–75). Boston, MA: Kluwer.

Ross, M. E. (2000). Science their way. *Young Children, 55*(2), 6–13.

Royce, C. A. (2007). Teaching through trade books: Rocking around the rock cycle. *Science & Children, 44*(5), 12–14.

Royce, C. A., & Wiley, D. A. (2005). The common ground: A rationale for integrating science and reading. *Science & Children, 42*(5), 40–42

Sanders, J., Patrick, J., Dedeoglu, H., Charbonnet, S., Henkel, M., Zhihui, F.,...Pringle, R. (2006–2007) Infusing reading into science learning. *Educational Leadership, 64*(4), 62–66.

Schlick Noe, K. L. (2004). *Extension projects: Literature circle resource center.* Retrieved from http://www.litcircles.org/Extension/extension.html

Schwartz, W. (1987). *Teaching science and mathematics to at risk students.* New York, NY: ERIC Clearinghouse on Urban Education. (ERIC Digest No. 289948)

Simon-Dudgeon, C., & Egbert, J. *Science as a second language: Verbal interactive strate gies help English language learners develop academic vocabulary.* National Science Teachers Association. Retrieved from: http://www.ncrel.org/sdrs/areas/issues/content/cntareas/math/ma7refer.htm

Smith and Welliver Educational Services. (2003). *Science process assessments for elementary and middle school students.* Retrieved from http://www.scienceprocesstests.com/

Straits, W., & Nichols, S. (2006). Literature circles for science. *Science & Children, 44*(3), 52–55.

Tally-Foos, K. (2005). Science alive! A full-day, all-school event brings community volunteers' perspectives on real world science. *Science & Children, 42*(4), 36–39.

U.S. Department of Education. (2000). *Before it's too late: A report to the nation from the national commission on mathematics and science teaching for the 21st century*. Jessup, MD: Education Publications Center.

U.S. Department of Education. Office of Educational Research and Improvement. (1993). *National excellence: A case for developing America's talent* (ED/OERI Publication No. 93–14). Washington, DC: U.S. Government Printing Office.

Van Zee, E. H., Iwasyk, M., Kurose, A., Simpson, D., & Wild, J. (2001). Student and teacher questioning during conversations about science. *Journal of Research in Science Teaching*, 38, 159–190.

Wood, J. (2005). *Discovery central. Science & Children, 42*(7), 36–37.

Yopp, H. K., & Yopp. R. H. (2006). Primary students and informational texts. *Science & Children, 44*(3), 22–25.

Responsive environments that provide high-end learning opportunities are essential for nurturing potential and closing the achievement gap.

Aber, J. L. (2007). Poverty and child development: Scientific advances and policy implications. Institute for Human Development and Social Change. New York University. Retrieved from http://www.google.com/url?sa=t&source=web&ct=res&cd=2&ved=0CA4QFjAB&url=http%3A%2F%2Fwww.speaker.gov%2Fpdf%2FAber.doc&ei=Q5CGS7zYB4mXtgem5MHGDw&usg=AFQjCNFYpelChM4jl71jXjermUSW8Kb_FQ

American Psychological Association. (2000). Resolution on poverty and socioeconomic status. *Roeper Review, 25*, 103–105.

Baldwin, A. Y. (2002). Culturally diverse students who are gifted. *Exceptionality, 10*, 139–147.

Bandura, A., Barbaranelli, C., Caprara, G. V., & Pastorelli, C. (2001). Self-efficacy beliefs as shapers of children's aspirations and career trajectories. *Child Development, 72*, 187–206.

Bernal, E. (2002). Three ways to achieve a more equitable representation of culturally and linguistically different students in GT programs. *Roeper Review, 24*, 82–88.

Bernal, E. M. (2003). To no longer educate the gifted: Programming for gifted students beyond the era of inclusionism. *Gifted Child Quarterly, 47*, 183–191.

Beyer, B. K. (1984). Teaching thinking skills: How the principal can know they are being taught. *NASSP Bulletin, 68*, 70–83.

Boothe, D., & Stanley, J. C. (Eds.). (2004). *In the eyes of the beholder: Critical issues for diversity in gifted education*. Waco, TX: Prufrock Press.

Bransford, J. D., Brown, A. L., & Cocking, R. R. (Eds.). (1999). *How people learn: Brain, mind, experience, and school*. Washington, DC: National Academies Press.

Burney, V. H., & Beilke, J. R. (2008). The constraints of poverty on high achievement. *Journal for the Education of the Gifted, 31*, 295–321.

Callahan, C. (2005). Identifying gifted students from underrepresented populations. *Theory Into Practice*, *44*, 98–104.

Cho, S., & Ahn, D. (2003). Strategy acquisition and maintenance of gifted and non-gifted young children. *Exceptional Children*, *69*, 497–505.

Cohen, L. (1990). *Meeting the needs of gifted and talented minority language students.* Retrieved from http://www.casenex.com/casenex/ericReadings/MeetingTheNeeds.pdf

Coleman, M. R. (1992). A comparison of how gifted/LD and average/LD boys cope with school frustration. *Journal for the Education of the Gifted*, 15, 239–265.

Coleman, M. R. (1994). Using cooperative learning with gifted students. *Gifted Child Today*, *17*(6), 36–38.

Coleman, M. R. (1996). Recognizing social and emotional needs of gifted students. *Gifted Child Today*, *19*(3), 36–37.

Coleman, M. R. (1998). Are we serious about meeting students' needs? *Gifted Child Today*, *21*(1), 40–41.

Coleman, M. R. (2001). Curriculum differentiation: Sophistication. *Gifted Child Today*, *24*(2), 24–25.

Coleman, M. R. (2001). Surviving or thriving? 21 gifted boys with learning disabilities share their school stories. *Gifted Child Today, 24*(3), 56–64.

Coleman, M. R. (2003). Four variables for success. *Gifted Child Today, 26*(1), 22–24.

Coleman, M. R. (2005). Cooperative learning and gifted learners. In F. A. Karnes & S. M. Bean (Eds.), *Methods and materials for teaching the gifted* (pp. 519–542). Waco, TX: Prufrock Press.

Coleman, M. R., & Coltrane, S. S. (2004). *Project U-STARS~PLUS: Science/Literature connections*. U-STARS at the University of North Carolina at Chapel Hill.

Coleman, M. R., & Gallagher, J. J. (1995) Appropriate differentiated services. *Gifted Child Today*, *18*(5), 32–33.

Coleman, M. R., & Nelson, S. M. (2001). Cooperative learning and gifted learners. In F. A. Karnes & S. M. Bean (Eds.), *Methods and materials for teaching the gifted* (3rd ed.; pp. 565–592). Waco, TX: Prufrock Press.

Coleman, M. R., Shah-Coltrane, S., Harradine, C., & Timmons, L. A. (2007) Impact of poverty on promising learners, their teachers, and their schools. In J. VanTassel-Baska & T. Stambaugh (Eds.), *Overlooked gems: A national perspective on low-income promising learners* (Section V, pp. 59–61). Washington, DC: National Association for Gifted Children.

Cross, T. L., & Burney, V. H. (2005). High ability, rural, and poor: Lessons from Project Aspire and implications for school counselors. *Journal of Secondary Gifted Education, 16,* 148–156.

Darity, W., Castellino, D., & Tyson, K. (2001*). Report on increasing opportunity to learn via access to rigorous courses and programs: One strategy for closing the achievement gap for at-risk and ethnic minority students.* Raleigh, NC: North Carolina Department of Public Instruction. Retrieved from http://www.ncpublicschools.org/docs/academicservices/gifted/resources/reports/increasingopportunities.pdf

Dweck, C. S. (1975). The role of expectations and attributions in the alleviation of learned helplessness. *Journal of Personality and Social Psychology, 31*, 674–685.

Dweck, C. S. (2007). The perils and promises of praise. *Educational Leadership*, *65*(2), 34–39.

The Education Trust. (2004). *A dream deferred: 50 years after Brown v. Board of Education, the struggle continues ... A 50 state look at achievement, attainment, and opportunity gaps.* Retrieved from http://www2.edtrust.org/EdTrust/Press+Room/2004+reports.htm

Ford, D. (1994). Nurturing resilience in gifted Black youth. *Roeper Review*, *17,* 80–85.

Ford, D. (2004). A challenge for culturally diverse families of gifted children: Forced choices between achievement or affiliation. *Multicultural*, *27*(3), 26–28.

Ford, D., Baytops, J., & Harmon, D. (1997). Helping gifted minority students reach their potential: Recommendations for change. *Peabody Journal of Education, 72*, 201–216.

Ford, D., Harris, J., III, Tyson, C., & Trotman, M. (2002). Beyond deficit thinking. *Roeper Review*, *24*, 52–58.

Ford, D., Howard, T., Harris, J., & Tyson, C. (2000). Creating culturally responsive classrooms for gifted African American students. *Journal for the Education of the Gifted, 23*, 397–427.

Ford, D. Y. (1992). Determinants of underachievement as perceived by gifted, above-average, and average black students. *Roeper Review, 14,* 130–136.

Ford, D. Y., & Grantham, T. C. (2003). Providing access for culturally diverse gifted students: From deficit to dynamic thinking. *Theory Into Practice, 42*, 217–225.

Ford, D. Y., & Moore, J. L., III (2004). Creating culturally responsive gifted education classrooms: Understanding "culture" is the first step. *Gifted Child Today*, *27*(4), 34–39.

Fraser, B. J., & Fisher, D. L. (1983). Development and validation of short forms of some instruments measuring student perceptions of actual and preferred classroom learning environment. *Science Education, 67,* 115–131.

Futrell, M. (2004, Summer). Anticipating success: Removing the barriers to educational equity and equality. *Harvard Journal of African American Public Policy, 10,* 103–116.

Gall, M. (1984). Synthesis of research on teacher's questioning. *Educational Leadership, 42(3),* 40–47.

Gallagher, J. (2005). The role of race in gifted education. *Roeper Review, 27,* 135.

Gallagher, J., Harradine, C. C., & Coleman, M. R. (1997). Challenge or boredom? Gifted students' views on their schooling. *Roeper Review, 19,* 132–136.

Hertzog, N. (2005). Equity and access: Creating general education classrooms responsive to potential giftedness. *Journal for the Education of the Gifted, 29,* 213–257.

International Reading Association and National Association for the Education of Young Children. (2000). *Learning to read and write: Developmentally appropriate practices for young children, Part 2.* Retrieved from http://www.naeyc.org/about/position/psread2.htm

Jensen, E. (1998). *Teaching with the brain in mind.* Alexandria, VA: Association for Supervision and Curriculum Development.

Kaplan, L. S. (1994). *Helping gifted students with stress management.* Retrieved from http://www.casenex.com/casenex/ericReadings/HelpingGiftedStudents.pdf

Kitano, M. (1989). The K–3 teacher's role in recognizing and supporting young gifted children. *Young Children, 44(3),* 57–63.

Kozleski, E. B., Sobel, D., & Taylor, S. V. (2003). Embracing and building culturally responsive practices. *Multiple Voices, 6*(1), 73–87.

Kuhn, D. (1986). Education for thinking. *Teachers College Record, 87,* 495–512.

Landis, M., Swain, K. D., Friehe, M. J., & Coufal, K. L. (2007). Evaluating critical thinking in class and online: Comparison of Newman Method and the Facione Rubric. *Communication Disorders Quarterly, 28*, 135–143.

Maroney, S., Finson, K., Beaver, J., & Jensen, M. (2003). Preparing for successful inquiry in inclusive science classrooms. *TEACHING Exceptional Children, 36*(1), 18–25.

Melber, L. (2003). Rainfall research. *Science and Activities, 39*(4), 10–15.

National Association for Gifted Children. (2008). *Teaching for high potential.* Retrieved from http://www.nagc.org/index.aspx?id=1498

National Center for Children in Poverty. (2006). *Basic facts about low-income children: Birth to age 18.* Retrieved from http://www.nccp.org/publications/pdf/text_845.pdf

National Research Council. (2002*). Minority students in special and gifted education.* Washington, DC: National Academies Press.

North Carolina Department of Public Instruction. (n.d.). *To Improve the achievement of under-performing students*. Retrieved from http://www.ncpublicschools.org/closingthegap/improve_achievement.html

Olszewski-Kubilius, P. (2003). Do we change gifted children to fit gifted programs, or do we change gifted programs to fit gifted children? *Journal for the Education of the Gifted, 26,* 304–313.

O'Neil, J. (2006). Beautiful minds. *NEA Today, 24*(4), 34–36.

Oxman, W. G. (1984). Thinking, basic skills, and learning. *American Education, 20*, 17–21.

Perkins, D. (1995). *Outsmarting IQ: The emerging science of learnable Intelligence*. New York, NY: Simon & Schuster.

Rogers, M. T., & Silverman, L. K. (n.d.) *Recognizing giftedness in young children.* Gifted Development Center, Denver, CO. Retrieved from http://eric.ed.gov/ERICDocs/data/ericdocs2sql/content_storage_01/0000019b/80/25/ae/96.pdf

Rubie-Davies, C. M. (2007). Classroom interactions: Exploring the practices of high and low expectation teachers. *British Journal of Educational Psychology, 77*, 289–306.

Samuels, C. (2005). N.C. program holds promise for gifted classes. *Education Week, 24*(40), 5.

Schunk, D. H., & Pajares, F. (2002). The development of academic self-efficacy. In A. Wigfield & J. S. Eccles (Eds.), *The development of achievement motivation* (pp. 15–31). New York, NY: Academic Press.

Seely, K. (2004). Gifted and talented students at risk. *Focus on Exceptional Children, 37*(4), 1–8.

Shaklee, B. D. (1995). Creating positive learning environments: Young gifted children at home and in school. *Understanding Our Gifted, 7*(3), 8–9.

Shore, B. M., & Dover, A. C. (1987). Metacognition, intelligence, giftedness. *Gifted Child Quarterly, 31*, 37–39.

Tamborini, R., & Zillman, D. (1985). Effects of questions, personalized communication style, and pauses of reflection in children's educational programs. *Journal of Educational Research, 79*, 19–26.

Tomlinson, C. A. (2002). Invitations to learn. *Educational Leadership, 60*(1), 7–10.

Tomlinson, C. A., Brighton, C., Hertberg, H., Callahan, C. M., Moon, T. R., Brimijoin, K., Reynolds, T. (2003). Differentiating instruction in response to student readiness, interest, and learning profile in academically diverse classrooms: A review of literature. *Journal for the Education of the Gifted, 27*(3), 119–145.

Tomlinson, C. A., Ford, D. Y., Reis, S. M., Briggs, C. J., & Strickland, C. A. (2004). *In search of the dream: Designing schools and classrooms that work for high potential students from diverse cultural backgrounds.* Washington, DC: National Association for Gifted Children.

Uresti, R., Goertz, J., & Bernal, E. J. (2002). Maximizing achievement for potentially gifted and talented and regular minority students in a primary classroom. *Roeper Review, 25,* 27–31.

U.S. Department of Education. (2007). *Status and trends in the education of racial and ethnic minorities.* (NCES 2007–039). Washington, DC: National Center for Education Statistics.

U.S. Department of Education. Office of Educational Research and Improvement. (1993). *National excellence: A case for developing America's talent* (ED/OERI Publication No. 93–14). Washington, DC: U.S. Government Printing Office.

Viadero, D. (2004, October). Panel outlines strategy for raising minority achievement. *Education Week, 24*(6), 10.

Vygotsky, L. (1978*). Mind in society: The development of higher psychological processes*. Cambridge, MA: Harvard University Press.

Weiss, P. F. (1988). *Review of literature on thinking for the research and evaluation committee of the consortium for the development of thinking for learning*. Chapel Hill, NC: Frank Porter Graham Child Development Center.

Wiegert, D. I., Kistner, J. A., Castro, R., & Robertson, B. (2001). Longitudinal study of young children's responses to challenging achievement situations. *Child Development, 72,* 609–624.

Zimmerman, B. J. (1990). Self-regulating academic learning and achievement: The emergence of a social cognitive perspective. *Educational Psychology Review, 2,* 173–201.

Teacher's systematic observations of students' strengths and abilities combined with documentation through student portfolios (work samples) provides a critical foundation to improve the identification of culturally/linguistic diverse and/or economically disadvantaged students for advanced educational opportunities.

Alexandrin, J. R. (2003). Using continuous constructive, classroom evaluations. *TEACHING Exceptional Children, 36*(1), 52–57.

Baldwin, A. Y. (1994). The seven plus story: Developing hidden talent among students in socioeconomically disadvantaged environments. *Gifted Child Quarterly, 38*, 80–84.

Bernal, E. (1981, February). *Identification of minority gifted students: Special problems and procedures.* Paper presented at the Council for Exceptional Children Conference, New Orleans, LA.

Bernard, B. (1993). Fostering resiliency in kids. *Educational Leadership, 19*(3), 44–48.

Boothe, D., & Stanley, J. C. (Eds.). (2004). *In the eyes of the beholder: Critical issues for diversity in gifted education.* Waco, TX: Prufrock Press.

Borland, J., Schnur, R., & Wright, L. (2004). Economically disadvantaged students in a school for the academically gifted: A post positivist inquiry into individual and family adjustment. *Gifted Child Quarterly*, *44*, 13–25.

Brighton, C. M. (2003). The effects of middle school teachers' beliefs on classroom practices. *Journal for the Education of the Gifted*, *27*, 177–206.

Bulterman-Bos, J., Terwel, J., Verloop, N., & Wardekker, W. (2002). Observation in teaching: Toward a practice of objectivity. *Teachers College Record*, *104*, 1069–1100.

Caffrey, E., Fuchs, D., & Fuchs, L. (2008). The predictive validity of dynamic assessment. *The Journal of Special Education, 41*, 254–270.

Carroll, J. B. (1997). Psychometrics, intelligence, and public perception. *Intelligence, 24*, 25–52.

Cassady, J. C., Neumeister, K. L. S., Adam, C. M., Cross, T. L., Dixon, F. A., & Pierce, R. L. (2004). The differentiated classroom observation scale. *Roeper Review*, *26*, 139–146.

Coleman, L. J. (1994). Portfolio assessment: A key to identifying hidden talents and empowering teachers of young children. *Gifted Child Quarterly, 38,* 65–69.

Coleman, M. R. (1992). A comparison of how gifted/LD and average/LD boys cope with school frustration. *Journal for the Education of the Gifted, 15*, 239–265.

Coleman, M. R. (1997). *New ways of seeing*. A video on multiple criteria for recognizing gifted students. [DVD] Available from STAGE FPG Child Development Center, UNC-CH 27599.

Coleman, M. R. (2005, Fall). With the eye of a teacher. *Teaching for High Potential*, 1–2.

Coleman, M. R., Harrison, A., & Shah, S. C. (2002). *Project U-STARS and STAGE: Harrison observation scale*. Chapel Hill, NC: U-STARS at the University of North Carolina at Chapel Hill.

Daniels, H., & Bizar, M. (1998). *Methods that matter: Six structures for best practice classrooms.* Portland, ME: Stenhouse.

Darity, W., Castellino, D., & Tyson, K. (2001). *Report on increasing opportunity to learn via access to rigorous courses and programs: One strategy for closing the achievement gap for at-risk and ethnic minority students* (Report No. ED459303). Raleigh, NC: North Carolina Department of Public Instruction.

Elhoweris, H. (2008). Teacher judgment in identifying gifted/talented students. *Multicultural Education*, *15*(3), 35–38.

Feiring, C., Louis, B., Ukeje, I., Lewis, M., & Leong, P. (1997). Early identification of gifted minority kindergarten students in Newark, NJ. *Gifted Child Quarterly, 41*, 76–82.

Ford, D., Baytops, J., & Harmon, D. (1997). Developing gifted minority students to reach their potential: Recommendations for change. *Peabody Journal of Education, 72*, 201–216.

Ford, D. Y. (1996). *Reversing underachievement among gifted black students: Promising programs and practices*. New York, NY: Teachers College Press.

Ford, D. Y., & Harris, J. (1990). On discovering the hidden treasure of gifted and talented black children. *Roeper Review, 13*, 27–32.

Frasier, J. J. (1991). Response to Kitano: The sharing of giftedness between culturally diverse and non-diverse gifted students. *Journal for the Education of the Gifted, 15*, 20–30.

Frasier, M. (1997). Gifted minority students: Reframing approaches to their identification and education. In N. Colangelo & G. Davis (Eds.). *Handbook of gifted education* (2nd ed., pp. 498–515), Boston, MA: Allyn & Bacon.

Gregory, D., Starnes, W., & Blaylock, A. (1998). *Finding and nurturing potential giftedness among Black and Hispanic students*. (Report No. EC 210641). East Lansing, MI: National Center for Research on Teacher Learning. (ERIC Document Reproduction Service No. ED 298707)

Griffin, J. B. (1992). Catching the dream for gifted children of color. *Gifted Child Quarterly, 36*, 126–139.

Hadaway, N., & Marek-Shroer, M. F. (1992). Multidimensional assessment of the gifted minority student. *Roeper Review, 15*, 73–77.

Han, K., Marvin, C., & Walden, A. (2003). Searching for an alternate way to identify young creative minds: A classroom-based observation approach. *Assessment for Effective Intervention*, *28*(2), 1–16.

Hodge, K. A., & Kemp, C. R. (2006). Recognition of giftedness in the early years of school: Perspectives of teachers, parents, and children. *Journal for the Education of the Gifted, 30*, 164–204.

Hodges, C. A. (1997, Winter). How valid and useful are alternative assessments for decision-making in primary grade classrooms? *Reading Research and Instruction*, *36*, 157–173.

Hojnoski, R. L., Gischlar, K. L., & Missall, K. N. (2009) Improving child outcomes with data-based decision making: Collecting data. *Young Exceptional Children*, *12*(3), 32–44.

Hosp, J. L., & Reschly, D. J. (2003). Referral rates for intervention or assessment: A meta-analysis of racial differences. *The Journal of Special Education, 37*, 67–80.

Hughes, C., Shaunessy, E., Brice, A., Ratliff, M., & McHatton, P. (2006). Code switching among bilingual and limited English proficient students: Possible indicators of giftedness. *Journal for the Education of the Gifted, 30*, 7–28.

Hunsaker, S. K. (1994). Adjustments to traditional procedures for identifying underserved students: Successes and failures. *Exceptional Children*, *61*, 72–76.

Jarosewich, T., Pfeiffer, S. I., & Morris, J. (2002). Identifying gifted students using teacher rating scales: A review of existing instruments. *Journal of Psychoeducational Assessment, 20,* 322–336.

Johnsen, S. (2007). Dispositions about gifted education. *Gifted Child Today, 30*(4), 5, 64.

Kaftan, J. M., Buck, G. A., & Haack, A. (2006). Using formative assessments to individualize instruction and promote learning. *Middle School Journal, 37*(4), 44–49.

Kearney, K., & LeBlanc, J. (1992). Forgotten pioneers in the study of gifted African Americans. *Roeper Review, 15,* 192–199.

Kirschenbaum, R. J. (1998). Dynamic assessment and its use with underserved gifted and talented populations. *Gifted Child Quarterly, 42,* 140–147.

Kitano, M. (1989). The K–3 teacher's role in recognizing and supporting young gifted children. *Young Children, 44*(3), 57–63.

Kitano, M. (1991). A multicultural educational perspective on serving the culturally diverse gifted. *Journal of the Education for the Gifted, 15,* 4–19.

Lee, L. (1999). Teachers' conceptions of gifted and talented young children. *High Ability Studies, 10,* 183–196.

Lee, O. (2005). Science education and student diversity: Synthesis and research agenda. *Journal of Education for Students Placed at Risk, 10,* 433–440.

Lidz, C. S., & Macrine, S. L. (2001). An alternative approach to the identification of gifted culturally and linguistically diverse learners. *School Psychology International, 22*(1), 74–96.

Lohman, D. (2005). Excerpted in review of Naglieri and Ford (2003): Does the Naglieri Nonverbal Ability Test identify equal proportions of high-scoring White, Black, and Hispanic students? *Gifted Child Quarterly, 49,* 19–28.

Lohman, D. F., Korb, K. A., & Lakin, J. M. (2008). Identifying academically gifted English-language learners using nonverbal tests. *Gifted Child Quarterly, 52,* 275–296.

Lohman, D. G. (2005). An aptitude perspective on talent: Implications for identification of academically gifted minority students. *Journal for the Education of the Gifted, 28,* 333–360.

Maker, C. J. (1996). Identification of gifted minority students: A national problem, needed changes and a promising solution. *Gifted Child Quarterly, 40*, 41–50.

McNair, S., Bhargava, A., Adams, L., Edgerton, S., & Kypros, B. (2003). Teachers speak out on assessment practices. *Early Childhood Education Journal, 31*, 23–31.

National Research Council. (2002). *Minority students in special and gifted education*. Washington, DC: National Academies Press.

Passow, A. H., & Frasier, M. M. (1996, February/March). Toward improving identification of talent potential among minority and disadvantaged students. *Roeper Review. 18*, 198–202.

Pfeiffer, S. I., & Jarosewich, T. (2007). The gifted rating scales-school form: An analysis of the standardization sample based on age, gender, race, and diagnostic efficiency. *Gifted Child Quarterly, 51*, 39–50.

Pfeiffer, S. I., & Petscher, Y. (2008). Identifying young gifted children using the gifted rating scales-preschool/kindergarten form. *Gifted Child Quarterly, 52*, 19–29.

Pierce, R. L., Adams, C. M., Speirs Neumeister, K. L., Cassady, J. C., Dixon, F. A., & Cross, T. L. (2007). Development of an identification procedure for a large urban school corporation: Identifying culturally diverse and academically gifted elementary students. *Roeper Review, 29*, 113–118.

Plucker, J. A., Callahan, C. M., & Tomchin, E. M. (1996). Wherefore are thou, multiple intelligences? Alternative assessments for identifying talent in ethnically diverse and low income students. *Gifted Child Quarterly, 40*, 81–92.

Reid, C., Romanoff, B., Algozzine, B., & Udall, A. (2000). An evaluation of alternative screening procedures. *Journal for the Education of the Gifted, 23*, 378–393.

Reiss, S., & Fogarty, A. (2006). Savoring reading schoolwide. *Educational Leadership, 64*(2), 32–36.

Rogoff, B., & Chavajay, P. (1995, October). What's become of research on the cultural basis of cognitive development? *American Psychologist, 50*, 859–877.

Sarouphim, L. M. (1999). DISCOVER: A promising alternative assessment for the identification of gifted minorities. *Gifted Child Quarterly, 43*, 244–251.

Scott, M., & Delgado, C. (2005). Identifying cognitively gifted minority students in preschool. *Gifted Child Quarterly, 49*, 199–210.

Scott, M. S., Perou, R., Urbano, R., Hogan, A., & Gold, S. (1992). The identification of giftedness: A comparison of White, Hispanic, and Black families. *Gifted Child Quarterly, 36*, 131–139.

Shaklee, B. (1992). Identification of young gifted students. *Journal for the Education of the Gifted, 15*, 134–144.

Smutny, J. F., Walker, S. Y., & Meckstroth, E. A.. (1997). *Teaching young gifted children in the regular classroom: Identifying, nurturing, and challenging ages 4–9*. Minneapolis, MN: Free Spirit.

Spicker, H. (1992). Identifying and enriching rural gifted children. *Educational Horizons, 70*, 60–65.

U. S. Department of Education. Office of Educational Research and Improvement. (1993). *National excellence: A case for developing America's talent* (ED/OERI Publication No. 93–14). Washington, DC: U. S. Government Printing Office.

VanTassel-Baska, J., Bass, G., Ries, R., Poland, D., & Avery, L. (1998). A national study of science curriculum effectiveness for high ability students. *Gifted Child Quarterly, 42*, 25–36.

VanTassel-Baska, J., Johnson, D., & Avery, L. D. (2002). Using performance tasks in the identification of economically disadvantaged and minority gifted learners: Findings from Project STAR. *Gifted Child Quarterly, 46*, 110–123.

Wright, L., & Borland, J. H. (1993). Using early childhood developmental portfolios in the identification and education of young, economically disadvantaged, potentially gifted students. *Roeper Review, 15*, 205–210.

Young, C., Wright, J., & Laster, J. (2005). Instructing African American students. *Education, 125*, 516–524.

Zappia, I. (1989). Identification of gifted Hispanic students: A multidimensional view. In C.J. Maker & S.W. Schiever (Eds.) *Critical issues in gifted education: Defensible programs for cultural and ethnic minorities* (pp. 19–26). Austin, TX: Pro-Ed.

Parental/family involvement directly impacts student success in school.

Allen, L., & Sethi, A. (2004). Bridging the gap between poor and privileged: How the parent-child home program uses books and toys to help poor toddlers succeed in kindergarten and beyond. *American Educator, 28*(2), 34–42, 54–55.

Boothe, D. & Stanley, J. C. (Eds.). (2004). *In the eyes of the beholder: Critical issues for diversity in gifted education.* Waco, TX: Prufrock Press.

Coleman, M. R., & Coltrane, S. S. (2004). *Project U-STARS: Family involvement packets*. Chapel Hill, NC: University of North Carolina at Chapel Hill.

Colombo, M. W. (2004). Family literacy nights and other home-school connections. *Educational Leadership, 61*(8), 48–51.

Cropper, C. (1998, January/February). Fostering parental involvement in the education of the gifted minority student. *Gifted Child Today, 21*(1), 20–24.

Darity, W., Castellino, D., & Tyson, K. (2001). *Report on increasing opportunity to learn via access to rigorous courses and programs: One strategy for closing the achievement gap for at-risk and ethnic minority students* (Report No. ED459303). Raleigh, NC: North Carolina Department of Public Instruction.

Diffily, D., & Fleege, P. O. (1994). The power of portfolios for communicating with families. *Dimensions of Early Childhood, 22*(2), 40–41.

Douglas-Hall, A., & Koball, H. (2004). *Low-income children in the United States*. Retrieved from http://www.nccp.org/pub_cpf04.html

Erion, J. (2006). Parent tutoring: A meta-analysis. *Education and Treatment of Children, 29*, 70–106.

Fielding, L. (2006). Kindergarten learning gap. *American School Board Journal, 193*(4), 32–34.

Ford, D., Baytops, J., & Harmon, D. (1997). Developing gifted minority students to reach their potential: Recommendations for change. *Peabody Journal of Education. 72*, 201–216.

Ford, D. Y., & Harris, J. J. (1999). *Multicultural gifted education*. New York, NY: Teachers College Press.

Greenspan, S. I. (2005). Assessing children for end-of-year profiles. *Early Childhood Today 19*(7), 16.

Hua, C. B., & Coleman, M. R. (2002). Preparing twice exceptional students for adult lives: A critical need. *Understanding Our Gifted, 14*(2),17–19.

Lopez, L. C. (1992, March 30–April 1). *Mexican-American and Angelo-American parental involvement with a public elementary school*. Paper presented at the National Conference on Creating the Quality School, Norman, OK.

National Research Council. (2002*). Minority students in special and gifted education*. Washington, DC: National Academies Press.

North Carolina Department of Public Instruction. (2002). *Closing the achievement gap in North Carolina: Movement in the village*. Raleigh, NC: Author.

Payne, R. K. (1996). *A framework for understanding poverty* (3rd. rev. ed.). Highlands, TX: aha! Process.

Ritblatt, W., Beatty, J., Cronan, T., & Ochoa, A. (2002). Relationships among perceptions of parent involvement, time allocation, and demographic characteristics: Implication for policy formation. *Journal of Community Psychology, 30*, 519–545.

Robertson, T. (2005). Parental guidance. *Crisis*. *112*(5), 26–29.

Scherer, M. (2002). Do students care about learning? – A conversation with Mihaly Csikszentmihalyi. *Educational Leadership*, *60*(1),12–17.

Shah, S. (2001). Project U-STARS schools aim to involve families with science. *Start Lights,* Spring.

Slocumb, P. D., & Payne, R. K. (2000). *Removing the mask: Giftedness in poverty*. Highlands, TX: aha! Process.

Taylor, J. (2005). Achieving excellence in urban schools: Pitfall, pratfalls, and evolving opportunities. *The Negro Education Review, 56*, 259–283.

U.S. Department of Education. Office of Educational Research and Improvement. (1993). *National excellence: A case for developing America's talent* (ED/OERI Publication No. 93–14). Washington, DC: U. S. Government Printing Office.

Young, J. G. (2002*). Parenting the creatively gifted.* Colorado, CO: Adventures in Creativity Publications.

Systemic change that is sustainable requires building an infrastructure that addresses personnel preparation, policies, curriculum, fiscal, and human resources.

Baker, B. D., & McIntire, J. (2003). Evaluating state funding for gifted education programs. *Roeper Review*, *25*, 173–179.

Baldwin, F. (2004, October). Proverbs represent life; therefore, there will be contradictory proverbs. *US Airways Attache*, 46–47.

Boothe, D., & Stanley, J. C. (Eds.). (2004). *In the eyes of the beholder: Critical issues for diversity in gifted education*. Waco, TX: Prufrock Press.

Bridges, R. E. (2001). *The North Carolina commission on raising and closing gaps: First report to the state board of education*. Raleigh, NC: The North Carolina Commission on Raising Achievement and Closing Gaps.

Briggs, C. J., Reis, S. M., & Sullivan, E. E. (2008). A National view of promising programs and practices for culturally, linguistically, and ethnically diverse gifted and talented students. *Gifted Child Quarterly*, *52*, 131–145.

Chamberlin, S. A. (2008). An examination of articles in gifted education and multicultural education journals. *Journal for the Education of the Gifted*, *32*, 86–99.

Coleman, M. R. (1998). Are we serious about meeting student needs? *Gifted Child Today*, *21*(1), 40–41.

Coleman, M. R. (2000). *Conditions for special education teaching: CEC commission technical report*. Arlington, VA: Council for Exceptional Children.

Council for Exceptional Children. (2001). *Bright futures for exceptional learners: An agenda to achieve quality conditions for teaching and learning*. Arlington, VA: Author.

Council for Exceptional Children. The Association for the Gifted. (2001). *Diversity and developing gifts and talents: A national action plan*. Arlington, VA: Author.

Darity, W., Castellino, D., & Tyson, K. (2001). *Report on increasing opportunity to learn via access to rigorous courses and programs: One strategy for closing the achievement gap for at-risk and ethnic minority students* (Report No. ED459303). Raleigh, NC: North Carolina Department of Public Instruction.

ERIC Clearinghouse on Tests, Measurement, and Evaluation, American Institutes for Research, Buros Institute of Mental Measurements, University of Nebraska-Lincoln. *Understanding achievement tests: A guide for school administrators.* Retrieved from http://openlibrary.org/b/OL2205717M/Understanding_achievement_tests

Feranchad, B., Ragona, A. J., Avichai, Y., Triana, A. (2002, July). *Quantitative evaluation of an intensive mathematics and science professional development intervention on student achievement.* Paper presented at the American Educational Research Association National Meeting, New Orleans, LA.

Fixsen, D. L., Naoom, S. F., Blasé, K. A.; Friedman, R. M., Wallace, F. (2005). *Implementation research: A synthesis of the literature.* Unpublished manuscript, National Implementation Research Network. Gainesville, FL: University of Florida.

Ford, D., Baytops, J., & Harmon, D. (1997). Developing gifted minority students to reach their potential: Recommendations for change. *Peabody Journal of Education, 72*, 201–216.

Gallagher, J. J. (1995). Education of gifted students: A civil rights issue? *Phi Delta Kappan, 76*, 408–410.

Gallagher, J. J. (2004). No child left behind and gifted education. *Roeper Review, 26*, 121–123.

Gollub, J. P., Bertenthal, M. W., Labov, J. B., & Curtis, P. C. (Eds.). (2002). *Learning and understanding: Improving advanced study of mathematics and science in U.S. high schools.* Retrieved from http://www.nap.edu/openbook.php?record_id=10129

Gusky, T. (2002). Does it make a difference? Evaluating professional development. *Educational Leadership, 59*(6), 45–51.

Horizon Research, Inc. (2006). *Local systematic change through teacher enhancement teacher questionnaire-science (Grades K–8).* Chapel Hill, NC: Author.

Jarvis, T., & Pell, A. (2004). Primary teachers' changing attitudes and cognition during a two-year science in-service programme and their effect on pupils. *International Journal of Science Education, 26*, 1787–1811.

Jolly, J., & Kettler, T. (2004). Authentic assessment of leadership in problem-solving groups. *Gifted Child Today*, *27*(1), 32–39.

Jost, K., (1997). Educating gifted students. *The CQ Researcher*, *7*(12), 265–288.

Kawasaki, K., & Herrenkohl, L. R. (2004). Theory building and modeling in a sinking and floating unit: A case study of third and fourth grade students' developing epistemologies of science. *International Journal of Science Education, 26*, 1299–1324.

Klingner, J. K., Ahwee, S., Pilonieta, P., & Menendez, R. (2003). Barriers and facilitators in scaling up research-based practices. *Exceptional Children, 69*, 411–429.

Kornhaber, M. (1999). Enhancing equity in gifted education: A framework for examining assessments drawing on the theory of multiple intelligences. *High Ability Studies, 10*(2), 143–161.

Kozleski, E. B., Sobel, D., & Taylor, S. (2003). Embracing and building culturally responsive practices. *Multiple Voices, 6*(1), 73–87.

Lee, H., & Songer, N. B. (2003). Making authentic science accessible to students. *International Journal of Science Education, 25*, 923–948.

Loucks-Horsley, S., Hewson, P., Love, N., & Stiles, K. (1998). *Designing professional development for teachers of science and mathematics*. Newbury Park, CA: Corwin Press.

Lowell, B. L., & Salzman, H. (2007). *Into the eye of the storm: Assessing the evidence on science and engineering education, quality, and workforce demand.* Retrieved from http://www.urban.org/UploadedPDF/411562_Salzman_Science.pdf

Martens, E. H. (1934). Selected references from literature on exceptional children. *Elementary School Journal, 34*(9), 277–323.

McBee, M. (2006). A descriptive analysis of referral sources for gifted identification screening by race and socioeconomic status. *The Journal of Secondary Gifted Education, 17*, 103–111.

Moore J. L., III, Ford, D. Y., & Milner, H. R. (2005). Recruitment is not enough: Retaining African American students in gifted education. *Gifted Child Quarterly, 49*, 51–67.

National Research Council. (2002*). Minority students in special and gifted education*. Washington, DC: National Academies Press.

National Science Teachers Association. (2008). *NSTA Reports*. Retrieved from http://www.nsta.org/publications/reports.aspx

National Staff Development Council. (2001). *National staff development council standards for staff development* (Rev.) Retrieved from http://www.nsdc.org/standard.htm

National Study Group for the Affirmative Development of Academic Ability. (2004). *All students reaching the top: Strategies for closing academic achievement gaps.* Retrieved from http://www.ncrel.org/gap/studies/thetop.htm

North Carolina Department of Public Instruction. (2000). *Closing the achievement gap: Views from nine schools*. Raleigh, NC: Author.

North Carolina Department of Public Instruction. (2001*). Closing the achievement gap: Voluntary assistance implementation guide 2001–2002*. Raleigh, NC: Author.

Popham, W. J. (1999). Why standardized tests don't measure educational quality. *Educational Leadership, 56*(6), 8–15.

Riggs, C. M., & Enochs, L. G. (1990). Toward the development of an elementary teacher's science teaching efficacy belief instrument. *Science Education, 74,* 625–637.

Roberts, J. K., & Henson, R. K. (2000, November). *Self-efficacy teaching and knowledge instrument for science teachers (SETAKIST): A proposal for a new efficacy instrument.* Paper presented at the Annual Meeting of the Mid-South Educational Research Association, Bowling Green, KY. (ERIC Document Reproduction Service, No. ED448208).

Robinson, A., Shore, B. M., & Enersen, D. L. (2007). *Best practices in gifted education, An evidence-based guide.* Waco, TX: Prufrock Press.

Robinson, N. M. (2003). Two wrongs do not make a right: Sacrificing the needs of gifted students does not solve society's unsolved problems. *Journal for the Education of the Gifted*, *26*, 251–273.

Romance, N., & Vitale, M. (2001). Implementing an in-depth expanded science model in elementary schools: Multi-year findings, research issues, and policy implications. *International Journal of Science Education, 23*, 373–404.

Siegle, D., & Powell, T. (2004). Exploring teacher biases when nominating students for gifted programs. *Gifted Child Quarterly*, *48*, 21–29.

Smith, P. (2002). *North Carolina's rural and small schools: Opportunities and challenges*. Greensboro, NC: North Carolina Association for Supervision and Curriculum Development.

Strong, S., Silver, H., & Perini, M. (1999). Keeping it simple and deep. *Educational Leadership, 56,* 22–24.

Swanson, J. (2006). Breaking through assumptions about low-income minority students. *Gifted Child Quarterly, 50,* 11–25.

Tomlinson, C. A., Coleman, M. R., Allan, S., Udall, A., & Landrum, M. (1996). Interface between gifted education and general education: Toward communication, cooperation, and collaboration. *Gifted Child Quarterly, 40,* 165–171.

U.S. Department of Education. Office of Educational Research and Improvement. (1993). *National excellence: A case for developing America's talent* (ED/OERI Publication No. 93–14). Washington, DC: U.S. Government Printing Office.

VanTassel-Baska, J., & Stambaugh, T. (2007, April). Overlooked gems: A national perspective on low-income promising learners. *Proceedings from National Leadership Conference on Low-Income Promising Learners.* Joint Publication of NAGC & Center for Gifted Education. Retrieved from http://www.nagc.org/uploadedFiles/Publications/Overlooked%20 Gems%20(password%20protected%20-%20gifted).pdf

Villegas, A. M., & Lucas, T. (2002). Preparing culturally responsive teachers: Rethinking the curriculum. *Journal of Teacher Education, 53,* 20–32.

Wadhwa, V. (2007, October 26). The science education myth. *Business Week*. Retrieved from http://www.businessweek.com/smallbiz/content/oct2007/sb20071025_827398.htm

Weiss, I. R., & Pasley, J. D. (2006, March). Scaling up instructional improvement through teacher professional development: Insights from the local systemic change initiative. *CPRE Policy Briefs*. March RB-44.

WestEd. (2004). When special education and general education unite, everyone benefits. *R & D Alert*, *6*(1), 1, 5, 8, 9.

Wyner, J. S., Bridgeland, J. M., & Diiulio, J. J. (2009). *Achievementrap: How America is failing millions of high-achieving students from lower-income families*. A Report from the Jack Kent Cooke Foundation. Retrieved from http://www.jkcf.org/assets/files/0000/0084/ Achievement_Trap.pdf